MIND AND

PERFORMANCE

A COMPARATIVE STUDY OF LEARNING IN MAMMALS, BIRDS, AND REPTILES

BY

HAROLD KENNETH FINK

VANTAGE PRESS, INC., NEW YORK

In memory of my father, Dr. Colin G. Fink, whose inspiration and encouragement helped make possible the five years of research on which this book is based.

FOREWORD

The purpose of publishing this book is, in part, to awaken the public—as well as certain scientists—to a greater awareness and appreciation of the capabilities of so-called "lower animals." One authority, Dr. Wilfred Funk, has published a dictionary of two hundred words whose meaning a dog is capable of learning. Muriel, Ernest P. Walker's pet monkey, has a fifty-word vocabulary in "monkey-talk."

The capacity of domestic and other animals is far beyond that which man has bothered to utilize. When, during a conversation, I mention that the pig learns faster than the dog, goat, chicken, rat, rabbit, or cat, my listener gives me that pained look which implies that I have rocks in my head. Because of biased, long-established stereotypes concerning sub-hominid animals, many people are unable to believe what animals can do if properly trained.

Just as our children require adequate education and supervision to realize their potential, so also do our working animals and pets need expert training in order to express their abilities and reach optimal adjustive harmony with man.

There is no excuse for a pet dog leaving muddy footprints on our guests' clothes. The fault lies not in the "stupidity" of a "dumb" animal, but in the carelessness of an owner too lazy to train his dog properly, so that he will not interfere with the rights of others.

A trained sheep dog can round up a herd quicker, more expertly, and with less nervous exhaustion on the part of the animals, than any human. . . . And we humans might envy the memory ability of some of the animals described in this book.

▼

PRECIS

IN THIS WORK THE CENTRAL PROBLEM WAS TO COMPARE THE learning ability of a fairly wide variety of animal forms, and particularly to determine the rate or speed of learning in one animal type in direct relation to that of other types. We were especially interested in comparing the learning performance of the turtle with that of certain higher vertebrates, including man.

For this purpose we considered the maze method to be the most advantageous for the reason that it does not require manipulatory performance of any kind. It was clear that, had such been required, those animals in the experimental series contemplated which did not possess prehensile members would be at an obvious disadvantage on that score. The method required only the animal's natural means of locomotion.

A simple maze, called the Arrow Maze, was employed. It consisted of four parallel pathways leading off from a neutral area wherein the animal was placed. At the end of one of the pathways or alleys, food was placed as an incentive in such a way that the animal could not see it until it had come to the end of the alley. The animal in the neutral starting area had to discover which of the paths led to the food and then had to learn that pathway.

The animals tested in this apparatus included man, domestic pig, dog, goat, white rat, chicken, rabbit, cat, and a selection of water turtles and land tortoises from both coastal regions of the United States.

The maze was simple enough to enable us to include the reptile class among the subjects, whereas a more complex learning situation might have necessitated the exclusion of this group, concerning which we were most interested. At the same time, the problem, presented to the subjects in the Arrow Maze, was such that it afforded a challenge for even the higher animals. The learning scores of the various animals which were obtained were diverse enough to differentiate clearly the species at different levels of the biological scale.

Four successive goals were presented for each subject to learn. This tended to neutralize the effects that may result from the customary use of a single goal. The animal, slow at first, has the chance to demonstrate its optimal performance in the learning of the later goals. If the subject should be somewhat timid at first in the strange apparatus, then a longer testing procedure, such as the one that we employed, would serve to remove this initial handicap to learning.

Three criteria of relative learning ability were used: the Performance Quotient (PQ), Trial Quotient (TQ), and Alley Quotient (AQ). These three measures of performance had a high intercorrelation, namely, .95. Each of these quotients employed the results for man as the standard, setting man's score arbitrarily at 100, so that all the other animals were thus related to the average value for man. The formulae which we devised for these three measures were constructed so as to give scores ranging from 0 to 100. The scores for each of the other animal subjects were thus *percentages* of the score for man.

Due to the reciprocal arrangement of the formulae, a large number of errors indicated a low PQ, TQ, or AQ score, depending upon the type of error in question. The PQ involved the total number of trials required for the animal to learn all four successive goals. The TQ employed this same value, but with the exclusion of all perfect trials among the incorrect ones. The AQ took into account the number of errors in the form of alleys entered while the animal was in search of the food at the goal. The average Q-score for each animal was the average of its PQ, TQ, and AQ scores.

In order to compare directly the learning performance of the slow-moving turtles with the higher vertebrates, time limits per trial in the maze were imposed upon each animal form in accordance with its relative rate of speed. For example, the chelonians were permitted 30 minutes in which to complete each trial (this figure being the standard of reference for the determination of the other values), while the more active dog was allowed only 1.3 minutes to find the food. The same maze and procedure was used in the case of all the animal forms with the exception of man. The human subjects were blindfolded and tested in a finger maze, bearing the same four-path pattern as the Arrow Maze. The criterion of successful learning for all subjects including man was a series of 10 successive correct trials to each goal without errors.

On the basis of the average Q-score for each species, the animals were ranked in order of ability of performance in the Arrow Maze. This rank order was as follows: man, pig, dog, chicken and rat (the latter two animal forms were at the same level), cat, two water turtle species (the Louisiana Troost Turtle and the Pacific Pond Turtle), and finally two land tortoises (the California Desert Tortoise, and the Common New Jersey Box Tortoise).

The above-mentioned animals included 151 of the subjects tested in the Arrow Maze. However, for the purpose of preliminary investigation, a few single specimens of other animals were employed. Two water turtle species, the Eastern Painted Turtle and the Louisiana Map Turtle, ranked above the four chelonian species already listed. Environmental and behavioral factors were suggested as possible causal factors for the apparent superiority of aquatic forms over the terrestrial chelonians.

A single goat and a rabbit were also tested. The goat ranked just below the dog and the rabbit placed above the cat.

The behavior of each animal form in the maze situation is described in the text. Although the males were slightly higher than the females in their average scores in the learning problem, the difference between the performance of the two sexes was not significant.

The first and second goals were learned in about the same length of time and number of trials. The third goal normally took a longer time to learn than the primary ones, but the final goal was learned in the shortest time of all.

Pavlov's concept of experimental extinction was suggested as an hypothesis to explain, at least in part, why the final goal in the Arrow Maze was generally learned in a shorter time than any of the preceding three goals, despite the chance that existed for interference and confusion with previous goals.

Learning curves for the three classes of animals studied (reptiles, birds, and mammals) were presented, and observable differences between them were noted. The reptile curve was more variable than the smoother learning curves of the birds and mammals.

In an additional experiment, results obtained with the Desert Tortoise in the Arrow Maze were compared with the performance of these subjects in certain other learning situations, namely, two problem boxes devised for these reptiles. It was found that the intercorrelation of *individual* performance in the three different learning problems was almost negligible. A specimen, proficient and relatively fast in escaping from one puzzle box, might, on the other hand, require a long time to learn the second problem box or the maze, and succeed only after an excessive expenditure of energy.

Supplemental data indicated that the reptiles which we studied possessed retention of a very stable sort. Few errors appeared in maze performance even after a lapse of more than a month and a half.

An analysis was made of the so-called "forward-going tendency" in the chelonians. It was discovered, statistically, that such a tendency actually did exist. On the other hand, evidence was lacking of a true and significant directional preference of the animals to the right or to the left in the maze situation.

It was suggested that the differences between the several animal forms in learning ability may be accounted for, in part, on a biological basis.

The question of the possible relation between intelligence, or capacity for performance, and relative level of metabolism was considered. This is an important consideration in the comparison of the learning performance of the reptile with that of the mammal, for example.

A series of graphic tracings of typical pathways taken by the animals in the maze is presented in the Appendix.

(Reprinted by permission of Cornell University. I wish to thank Professors O. D. Anderson and G. L. Kreezer for helpful suggestions and advice, and the estate of Professor Harold Hibbert for financial aid.)

CONTENTS

I. IN RETROSPECT

THE CHIEF PURPOSE OF THE PRESENT INVESTIGATION HAS BEEN to compare directly the learning behavior of the turtle (a selection of a few representative land and water turtles from both the Atlantic and Pacific Coasts) with that of certain higher vertebrates, including man, in an experimentally devised situation which was essentially the same for each type of animal employed.

A survey of much of the literature concerned with animal behavior, and particularly that dealing with the various learning performances of animals, reveals three interesting facts. First, it is clear that little experimental work upon learning behavior has been done in the case of the turtle. Second, it is equally apparent that there have been no studies designed specifically to compare the learning reactions and capacities of this animal with those of higher vertebrates. And finally, speaking generally, there has been little valid comparative work relating various animals. The reason for this is a lack of uniformity of procedure and equipment in the case of different animal forms, even in the hands of a single investigator. And there is naturally a lack of uniform procedure for various animals when one compares the work of different investigators.

Due to these facts, therefore, it is extremely difficult for those interested in Comparative Psychology to find in the literature entirely valid and clear-cut comparisons of diverse animals. For it is obvious that the reactions of a cat

1

in a problem box cannot be compared directly with those of a rat in a maze or with those of a dog in the conditioned reflex chamber. Literature on the subject clearly shows the need for more investigations of a type designed to compare the behavior of different animals in the same experimental setup.

We shall now present a brief survey of the literature pertinent to our problem. Because of the emphasis which we have chosen to direct upon the reptile class in this study, we shall first consider research on learning in the turtle. Following this, we shall deal with comparative work of single investigators on several animal forms, tested within the same apparatus.

Prior to the present study, no comparative work has been attempted on chelonians or other reptiles. Noncomparative psychological work on turtles is presented chronologically below.

Yerkes, in 1901,[1] employed the maze method to test the learning speed of an eastern water turtle, *Clemmys guttata*. One of his mazes had 4 cul-de-sacs, the other had 6, as well as a section of pathways leading up and down an incline. Instead of by food, which Yerkes found an inadequate incentive for this turtle, the single specimen was motivated by escape from bright illumination and from confinement, and by the attainment of the goal, a dark nest box. In the first maze, trial #1 was completed by the animal in 35 minutes, but 20 trials reduced the time to only half a minute. In the more difficult maze, 90 minutes was necessary for the first trial, this figure being reduced to 4 minutes in 20 trials. At trial #50, the required time to complete the course of the maze still remained in the neighborhood of 4 minutes, indicating that this was probably the optimal speed for the turtle in this particular maze.

The obvious conclusions from Yerkes' work seem to be that a turtle can improve its performance in a maze situation by avoiding blind alleys, as a consequence of which there results a saving of steps and of time. Further evidence of

---

[1] Numbers refer to References, pp. 111 ff.

adaptive performance is indicated by the interesting fact that the turtle gradually learned to skip most of the descending ramp by simply "jumping off" the incline in the direction of the nest box, thus shortening the pathway to the goal.

Casteel, in 1911,[2] used the discrimination box technique in his careful study of visual acuity in the Central Painted Turtle, *Chrysemys picta marginata*. This Midwestern species is aquatic like *Clemmys guttata* mentioned above. A total of 7 specimens acted as subjects for the various experiments. An achromatic card of alternating black and white lines was attached to a box at the end of each alley of the discrimination apparatus. In each trial, food was available in one box, and a shock was administered in the other box. To obtain food and to avoid receiving the electric shock, the turtle had to demonstrate visual discrimination between different pairs of cards, during each series of conditioning trials. In spite of shocks accompanying many incorrect responses, some of the animals developed persistent position habits, necessitating their disqualification from further experiment.

The Painted Turtle distinguished horizontal from vertical lines and also vertical lines of 3 mm. width from similar lines of 2 mm. width, a difference of only 1 mm. (Furthermore, the turtles displayed good retention of these problems after a period of four months.) However, two patterns, "star" and "Maltese cross" respectively, could not be distinguished, probably because they had the same total area of blackness and also because they were so very similar in spatial arrangement and size. Conforming to the main theme of our present study, *i.e.* comparative learning performance, the essential question is whether the turtle, in a discrimination box, can be conditioned successfully to employ in a consistent manner whichever pathway in a particular trial leads to the attainment of the reward, while at the same time avoiding the path, the stimulus for which predicts ultimate punishment. Casteel has clearly demonstrated that this is indeed possible in a reptile.

Parschin, in 1929,[3] succeeded in establishing a conditioned reflex (CR) to light stimulation in turtles. The unconditioned reflex upon which the CR was based was the withdrawal movement of the animal's head when the head was tapped lightly. About 300 combinations of light and tapping were necessary to set up a durable and constant CR. A colored light was clearly differentiated from a white light in a later series in this experiment.

Tinkelpaugh, in 1932,[4] with the use of a five-section multiple-T maze, demonstrated exceptionally fast learning in a single turtle specimen. The animal learned to run the maze without error in only 4 trials.

Thus it is evident from the above studies that the chelonians show evidence of maze-learning ability, successful visual discrimination, and conditioning.

No work comparing turtles with higher vertebrates is to be found in previous literature. There were, however, a few investigations, wherein comparison of performance was made between higher forms in the same apparatus.

Hamilton, in 1911,[5] employed the multiple-choice technique to test the relative learning performance in different species of animals. The same apparatus—an enclosure ending in 4 exits obstructed by closed doors—was used with all the animals. With each successive trial, a different door leading to food was left unlocked. The number of locked doors touched in the course of a hundred trials was recorded. The same exit was never used for two trials in succession; apparently, this is one of the rules of performance which the more intelligent animals quickly learned. The rank order of proficiency in the apparatus from best performance to poorest was as follows: man, monkey, dog, cat, and finally the horse. Only the horse displayed stereotyped behavior by repeatedly attempting to push open the same wrong door.

Jenkins' Triple-Plate Problem Box, described by him in 1927,[6] was employed by Shuey,[7] Riess,[8] Field,[9] and Koch[10] in the years between 1931 and 1935 to compare the performance of the monkey, cat, and two species of rodents. Jenkins' apparatus had three depressible plates which had to be stepped upon in correct succession in order to open the food compartment door in the center of the box. Ability was measured in terms of the optimal number of steps attained by any individual of a particular species. These so-called "steps" or separate problems were defined as follows:

The attainment of step #1 indicated that the animal had learned to depress the first floor plate in order to obtain food. If the animal was capable of attaining step #2, this meant that he was able to learn to depress plates #1 and #2 in that order, before being permitted to enter the food compartment. A great number of possible steps is obtainable with this puzzle box if one employs the simple expedient of continuing the serial order of learned plates in reverse. For instance, in step #4, the three brass plates would be pressed in the order of 1-2-3-2, to meet the criterion of success, while step #6 would read 1-2-3-2-1-2.

The following rank order of animal ability, resulting from the combined researches above, indicates the highest point reached by any one of 20 to 35 animals of each type tested. These included monkeys (step #22), cats (step #7), white rats (#2), and guinea pigs (#1, only).

Liddell, James, and Anderson, in 1934,[11] published the results of a long-time experimental program of study at the Cornell Behavior Farm dealing, among other things, with the rate of acquisition of a conditioned motor reflex (CMR) in various animals. Flexion of the left foreleg in several specimens of each of the five mammals, namely, the dog, pig, sheep, goat, and rabbit, was conditioned by a 435 cycle tone followed by an electric shock. This procedure was repeated until the first occurrence of the CMR, and then continued further in order to determine the stability of the responses, *i.e.* how many repetitions of the associated stimuli were necessary before the CMR would appear *every* time.

James, in 1934,[12] and in 1937,[13] published the results of work in the same laboratory, employing similar apparatus under identical conditions. James attempted to establish the same CMR on 5 guinea pigs and 3 opossums.

Although the two investigations cited above were not primarily studies of learning as such, the present writer be-

lieves that the results imply a rank order of animals in respect to the speed of learning a CR. The different types of
animals acquired this specific CMR in the following order of
speed: the pig first, closely followed by the dog. Not much
slower than the dog were the sheep and the goat on about the
same level, while a large drop in the learning-performance
level seemed to exist between these latter animals and the
rabbit. The guinea pig was very much slower in attaining the
reaction pattern, while the opossum never succeeded at all.

The first appearance of the leg flexion occurred in the
second trial for the pig, from the third to the fifth trial for
the dog, while for both the sheep and the goat the CMR appeared in either the seventh, eighth, or ninth trial. The rabbit required 14 to 24 repetitions of signal and shock, and
the guinea pig 100+ repetitions.* The opossum, on the other
hand, had to be given up as an experimental subject, because
of its tendency to curl up in a ball and refuse to react in any
other way. This latter behavior, of course, may not at all
imply lack of learning ability, but simply the particular
behavior that this species has learned to employ in such a
frustrating, restrictive, or annoying situation. As to the stability of the acquired response, the pig, for example, needed
on the average 20 repetitions of the stimuli before the CR
consistently appeared, the sheep required 36 repetitions,
while the rabbit never attained a stable response.

There are, perhaps, other comparative studies in the
literature, and we may have inadvertently omitted them,
but we shall now give an example of a comparative study in
which the question of *interpretation* of the results is not an
easy matter. This is not intended as destructive criticism of
the work. We merely wish to point out a difficulty that the
comparative psychologist all too frequently encounters.

Like Hamilton five years previously,[5] Yerkes, in
1916,[14,15] employed the method of multiple choice. His
study included the crow, rat, pig, monkey, and ape. The

---

* The CMR of the left foreleg of the guinea pig was never truly specific.
The movements of other parts of the body were included in the response

fact that only two monkeys and one ape were employed may account, in part, for the difficulty in satisfactorily comparing primates in this study with other species tested. To each of the subjects, Yerkes presented problems of increasing difficulty.

In problem #1, the food in each trial was to be found only in the left-hand box of each group or series of boxes displayed. These arrangements of boxes were, of course, altered each time as is customary in this method. Learning is not, therefore, of a specific goal, but of a relative goal whose position bears a constant relationship to other objects. The incentive in problem #2 was concealed in the second box from the right end of each group. Alternation of the incentive location from left to right end, and back to left again, comprised problem #3. Most difficult, apparently, was the final problem #4, in which the middle box of each series contained the food.

The single ape, a young orangutan, solved problem #1 in 290 trials, but was unsuccessful in solving problem #2, after 1380 practice attempts. The monkeys proved more successful than the single ape. This is surprising considering the relative phyletic standing of apes and monkeys. One monkey, *Macacus rhesus*, learned problem #1 in only 70 trials and needed 400 trials in order to learn problem #2. The other monkey, *Macacus irus*, learned the first two problems in 132 and 1070 trials, respectively.

The best performance, however, was evidenced by the pigs which completed problem #1 in 50 trials or less, problem #2 in 390 to 600 trials, problem #3 in 420 to 470 trials. Problem #4 proved too difficult, the criterion of success not being reached in 800 trials. The crows had a range of 50-100 trials in the learning of problem #1, but in the course of 500 trials they did not learn the next problem. White rats failed to learn problem #2; moreover, the rats needed three or four times as many trials (170-350) as the crows to learn the first problem.

To take these results at face value would rank the pig, which completed the first three problems, higher than the monkey, which solved only two of the experimental situations. The monkey, in turn, would rank higher than the ape, which finished only one problem. Omitting the insufficient data on the monkeys and the single ape, we may say with greater certainty that the results, in agreement with the work of others mentioned in the present report (see under V. Discussion), indicate that the pig, the crow (birds in general, possibly), and the white rat had this rank order of ability.

Possibly the ape was poorly motivated and not too interested in the food incentive. This might explain his inferior performance, which is inconsistent with the evidence of superior manipulation of sticks and other objects in supposedly ideational problems of need satisfaction. Yerkes, himself,[15] presents some data on such rational behavior in this particular ape, which was not found in the two monkeys.

On the other hand, the multiple-choice method does not seem to test the same constellation of factors that, for example, maze-learning experiments test. Concerning the multiple-choice method of testing learning ability, Maier and Schneirla[16] offer the following verdict:

> In general, higher vertebrates are more capable in multiple-choice problems than lower forms, but the order of ability is inconsistent. The method is inadequate for demonstrating the presence or nature of higher processes.

In the brief survey above, we have dealt with the comparative learning ability of different animals, as tested by the multiple-choice method, problem box, and the conditioned response technique. We are unable to find valid comparative work, employing the maze method, probably because of the discouraging difficulties in obtaining equivalent conditions for animals possessing different locomotor systems, phyletic level, and size.

It is evident from a perusal of the literature in general that considerable confusion exists concerning the relative abilities of different animals. Some of this confusion undoubtedly is due to the variety of learning methods and criteria employed by various researchers. Therefore, we have designed the present experiment in such a way that the learning abilities of several different animals can be tested with the same apparatus, involving a problem which is capable of solution by animals fairly low in the biological scale (in this case, turtles), yet difficult enough so that the higher animals employed could demonstrate superior performance.

Before discussing the method employed in this investigation, it should be made clear that the present study is not a statistical problem. It is a preliminary investigation in which relatively small numbers of animals of each species were used. This limitation of numbers was made necessary in this initial study by the consideration of time, finance, and the availability of subjects. The great length of time absorbed by the turtle experiments alone can be readily appreciated by those familiar with the energy level and the resultant slow rate of speed of this reptile. It is hoped that further work along these lines may be stimulated, and that such work will fill in the necessary gaps and omissions.

Thus it is the design of the present work to contribute not only data on learning behavior in the turtle, but data on a direct comparison of this animal's learning performance with that of other vertebrate forms. These include man, dog, cat, domestic pig, white rat, and chicken. In this study, we have employed essentially the same procedure and equipment in the case of all the animal forms.

II. METHOD

IN THE PRESENT INVESTIGATION, THE MAZE METHOD OF STUDY-ing animal learning was chosen as being the most advantageous for our purpose.

We employed a maze, four-foot square, for all the animals we shall herewith discuss (see Fig. 1). The Arrow Maze was christened after the median design of the pattern.

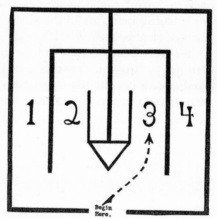

Fig. 1. *The Arrow Maze, with the path toward the first goal indicated by the arrow. (The gap in the front partition of the maze is the location of the entrance arch.)*

It was planned and built by the author, while at Pasadena, California. The first subjects were specimens of the California Desert Tortoise, *Gopherus agássizii* (Fig. 2), on which species the author spent the most time and effort in the present research.

Our quest lay in the direction of a simple problem situation, adaptable for our entire proposed list of animal subjects, and likewise for specimens of different size (within certain rational limits). Considerations of a purely practical nature were not overlooked. The final design of the maze was such that the apparatus could be constructed easily, carried from place to place, and readily dismantled, folded up and put out of the way when not in use. This very simple maze, which could be quickly duplicated by any research worker, was used in such a way as to combine aspects of both a maze situation and a discrimination procedure. That the animal subject was permitted to wander freely in the pathways till the incentive (food appropriate for the particular species employed) was discovered may be considered an aspect of maze procedure. That there was no complex route to the goal, on the other hand, but merely four possible alleys from which to choose, opening from a common neutral area in front of the maze, adds to the method a taste of discrimination box procedure.

The outer boards of the maze, when necessary, could be spread a few inches laterally in order better to accommodate the larger animals (the two-months-old goat and some of the larger species of dogs), without changing the alley distances or altering the maze pattern. The partitions consisted of upright pine boards 11 inches high, and mutually connected and fastened by hinges and hooks. All the partitions of the maze were painted a uniform black. The floor of the apparatus consisted of disposable white paper which, by means of reflection, afforded improved illumination of the pathways from the lamp directly above the center of the maze and the room lights overhead. In the front panel of the Arrow Maze was a doorway carved in the shape of an arch large enough for placing the smaller animals, such as the rodents and the turtles, into the maze. This opening had a sliding wooden door, also painted black, to conceal the entrance from the animal inside the maze, and to prevent escape. The alleys or pathways were numbered from one to four, reading from left to right in the figure (Fig.1), alley #3 being the correct alley-path to the first goal which the animal had to learn.

We selected alley #3—although #2 could have served as well—because of its nearness to the entrance. This proximity made the first learning problem less difficult, and it was planned in this manner so as not to discourage the animal at the very outset.*

The criterion for success in learning each alley was a perfect series of 10 successive trials to the designated goal, without errors in the form of wandering into other alleys. Although some experimenters prefer a 9-out-of-10 trial criterion (to save time and to compensate for "imperfect learners"), for certain practical reasons the author decided to use a 10-out-of-10 criterion as the measure of success. Not the least of these reasons was the obvious simplification of the mathematical treatment that the latter technique afforded.

Following the completion of the learning of alley #3, alley #2 became the goal site, and food was placed only in this latter alley. The experimental animal was now confronted with the task of unlearning the recently acquired habit of passing to the right of the maze entrance for food, and had to form a new or revised pattern of behavior in the sinistral direction. The goal location was placed again in the dextral half of the maze, in alley #4. With the final goal, alley #1, the subject had to alter his behavior for the second time from a tendency to go right to a habit of going left.

This alteration of direction in our study was planned so as to prevent, during the learning process, the formation of

---

* This point is particularly important in the case of chelonians, because of their low-energy reserve, and their consequently restricted rate of locomotion. If the problem proves too difficult, the turtle may stop acting within the experimental setup and, instead, withdraw to a corner, or else endlessly struggle to escape by scraping and pushing against the maze wall. On the other hand, if it finds the food on the very first trial, the increased intensity of the animal's motivation becomes evident in the faster tempo of its behavioral manifestations.

1 cm

1 inch

Fig. 2. The California Desert Tortoise, GO-PHERUS AGASSIZII. A drawing from life of B-1, one of the smaller members of this species tested in the Arrow Maze.

position habits which might have distorted our final picture. Animals that may have employed kinesthetic clues more than visual or other higher faculties, in the performance of the maze routine, were therefore not greatly aided by such behavior. Although kinesthesis might unconsciously aid the animal to learn a single goal, thereafter it would prove more of a handicap, since it would interfere with learning the goals located in the opposite direction. On the basis of the above consideration, one may hypothesize that the slower animals, such as the turtles, probably are slow because they depend more on kinesthetic factors than on other clues, such as local signs of distance and direction. However, enticing as it may seem, the present study can offer no basic experimental proof of such an assumption, since the role of kinesthesis was not investigated in our animals.

The order of the locations of the successive goals was, therefore, 3-2-4-1 for all animals. The statistical minimum number of trials for any subject totaled 40, *i.e.* 10 perfect successive trials to each of the four alleys, or goals.

The reasons for having four alternate goals rather than one, as is customary in maze work, were as follows: A repetition of performance in the maze is demanded of the animal because the end result for each subject is believed to afford a more accurate analysis of his relative speed of learning and his behavioral responses to new situations than would be possible if the result of performance were restricted to a single goal. The Arrow Maze offers the chance to test learning, and also relearning, without necessitating the alteration of either the maze pattern or the basic type of problem presented to the animal. Chance passage of the subject directly to the first goal, in his initial encounter with the maze, does not necessarily weight the animal's final score in a favorable direction. Furthermore, it does not handicap other subjects, since no single trial or brief series of trials is all-important in the final reckoning, but only the complete run of trials. Only the sum total of performance values to all four goals determines the learning score in the present study. Moreover, in the majority of cases, we observed that a perfect first trial of the naïve animal in the maze rarely was succeeded by a second trial of the same kind until after much exploration of other pathways had been accomplished. The animal does not settle down to maintaining a strict and distinct path to the goal until it first has satisfied its insistent motive of curiosity concerning the newly imposed environment, and its consequent urge to explore this region. Fortuitous behavior of the type mentioned above is normally balanced, through the law of averages, by lesser "luck" in the later trials. None of our experimental animals ever has consistently entered the correct pathway immediately following each change of the goal location.

Another advantage of the multi-goal method is that those animals of an initially timid nature, such as the goat and the rabbit which we employed, will not be handicapped by slower trials in the very beginning. These early scores will tend to be balanced by the later performance of the animals in the other three alleys. The animal has the chance to demonstrate improvement through the intelligent use of past experience gained in the previous practice trials. After learning the first goal, it can profit by this new knowledge of the general maze routine by learning the second goal in less time. Indeed, this is what usually happens.

Furthermore, the statistical advantage of four goals over one is obvious. A multi-goal problem necessitates a longer learning period, more days, and more trials. The occasional, atypical spurts or regressions in learning tend to be neutralized. A temporary handicap, affecting the animal on a particular day, would not have the weight or importance in the final results that it would have in a much shorter test.

A screen was not placed over the maze during the animal's progress. Such a cover, because it would induce a greater feeling of confinement in the animal, would only tend to incite fear and lead him to seek escape from the maze. A covering would also lessen the animal's visibility at the very time when the experimenter was busily occupied with the task of recording the pathway which the animal followed, and the time of the subject's arrival at the goal.

The route of the animal in each trial was drawn,* in order to facilitate the later analysis of the animal's behavior. From this drawing of the path taken by the animal in a particular trial, the numerical record of the route was derived. For example, if the goal was in alley #3, 2-1-3 (abbreviated in our own records "213") would indicate that the animal in this trial entered alleys 2, 1, and 3 in that order.

The duration of each trial was determined by means of a "Time-It,"† which, for convenience, was especially wired to a box fitted with a toggle switch. The time for each trial was recorded to the nearest tenth of a minute. Only the total running time, absorbed in actual searching for food or exploration of pathways, was included in the recorded time for each trial. (The timer was snapped off if the animal became quiescent, unless such inactivity proved persistent or "permanent" as in some of the first trials of the less readily motivated chelonian group.)

The food incentive was concealed within the maze in such a way that the subject could not perceive it until he came upon it during a successful trial. For alley #2 or #3, the food was situated within the central partitions bordering the "arrow pattern." For the remaining goals, the food was concealed in the rear of the maze. (A glance at Fig. 1 will make this clear.)

To obtain an indication of the comparative performance of a reptile in different types of learning apparatus, two problem boxes, presenting different complications, were used with one of the chelonian species, the Desert Tortoise (Fig. 2). They were appropriately designated the Trip Box and the Ring Box. In the Trip Box, the animal found itself in an enclosure from which there was no immediately ap-

---

* The first and second trials of a representative member of each species is depicted in the Appendix.

† Manufactured by the Precision Scientific Co., 1750 No. Springfield Ave., Chicago, Illinois. Time to the nearest hundredth of a minute can be read from the clear dial of this instrument. (A stop watch, on the other hand, is less easily handled and can be read only in inconvenient units which must then be converted to the metric system.)

parent escape. The walls were wood, thus preventing visibility and increasing the sense of confinement that the Desert Tortoise seemed to resist.

This factor, together with the desire for food, increased the motivation to escape. At the front end of this elongated box was a door, hinged at the base, which, when properly released, fell outward upon the floor. Restraining the door was a weight held in a groove in the top of the board. This weight was attached to a spring which held a wire taut. The wire curled around a hook at the base of the box on the inner right side. The animal had to step on the wire to release it from the hook which then permitted the door to fall open with the aid of the weight on top. Either the head, the foot, or the gular extension of the tortoise's plastron could be employed to press down the wire and thus effect escape to the food outside. Because of the variety of methods of working the "trip mechanism," this problem box was the easier of the two, and more often permitted success on the first trial.

The Ring Box, on the other hand, demanded more exact manipulation of a metal ring attached to a door catch by means of a wire running over a pulley at the top of the box. When the tortoise placed a foreleg or its head into the ring and pressed the ring downward, the door opened outward in the same fashion as in the Trip Box, and lay flat on the floor, thus enabling the animal to walk out over it to reach the food. The first trial-and-error attempts in the Ring Box, because of the relatively greater difficulty for reptiles, often proved unfruitful, but in time success was attained.

Certain appropriate sizes of the Desert Tortoise (large and strong enough to work the wires) were tested in both puzzle boxes, as well as in the Arrow Maze, and the three sets of data were compared (see IV. Quantitative Results). The negative results (i.e. the very low correlation between relative success in the three learning situations) would seem to offer a clear-cut example of a difficulty already mentioned. That is the lack of validity that tends to exist in tests of animals in different types of apparatus. Proficiency in one learning apparatus does not necessarily imply ability in all types of learning problems.

However, on the other hand, had the Desert Tortoise been compared with the dogs and other higher vertebrates in the puzzle boxes, we would expect to find a rank order of ability similar to that which had been found in the Arrow Maze.

Man was taken as the standard of reference for the scoring of all maze work. Fifty college students of both sexes volunteered to run the maze "in miniature." A Finger Maze of masonite board with wire partitions on its surface was employed. The pattern of this hominid maze was essentially the same as that of the Arrow Maze, with the addition of a starting point for the finger of the subject.

The subject sat blindfolded at a table before the Finger Maze, and travelled along the pathways between the wires by the use of the index finger of the right hand. The blindfold was considered necessary in order to prevent the human subjects from having the advantage of perceiving the whole pattern at a glance. The animals in the floor maze had no such aid in the pursuance of the maze routine, since they were able to see only that part of the pathways visible from their particular location at a given moment.

The essential part of our instructions to each human subject was as follows: "I am putting your finger at the entrance to an enclosure, bordered by these partitions which you can feel. (Demonstrated by passing the subject's finger along one of the wire walls.) My instructions are simply to follow the path, to travel at will within the enclosure, but without crossing any of the partitions."

After some wandering through the alleys, the subject's finger will eventually enter what corresponds to alley #3 in the floor maze. The subject, at this moment, was asked to pause for further instructions: "You have reached a goal within the enclosure, and I will inform you each time that you do so again. My verbal response will indicate that you have been temporarily successful in your activities. After you reach the goal each time, I will lift your finger and return it to the entrance point, so that you can start again. You may travel anywhere within the enclosure and as fast as you like."

As pointed out above, all of the 50 human subjects were young, being of college age. This conformed to the general stipulation that only young subjects, whether human or animal, be used. Young subjects were preferred because it was thought that they might show a somewhat higher degree of motivation, interest, and willingness to serve. Naturally, it was considered necessary to control the age factor, in so far as possible, since this control is not only conventional in experiments of this sort, but it is also essential to a clear-cut interpretation of the results. Of course, approximate age equivalents for the various animal forms, rather than actual age in years, were considered.

There are further specific reasons for the use of young subjects. The age of young animals is usually better known, especially in the reptile class. In the case of older animals in this class, the determination of approximate age is little more than guesswork. The determination is usually made from size and other physical characteristics.

Some Desert Tortoises found on the Mojave Desert in California may be 100 or even 200 years old.* Apparently, they live an indeterminate number of years if unmolested in their natural environment, and provided, of course, that their simple needs of life remain available. Most of the tortoise's life is spent in sleeping or basking in the sun. The meager expenditure of energy necessary for the attainment of food probably accounts, to a large degree, for the fact that this species and the related and similarly structured *Testudo vicini* of the Galapagos Islands live to such an extreme old age.

There is, in addition, a purely practical reason for employing younger animals in a maze of this sort. This is the obvious fact that the younger specimens are smaller, and

---

* This is a prediction based on their very slow growth rates, concerning which an elaborate account will be published elsewhere.

therefore occupy less room in the maze and cages during the process of experiment. Important from a psychological standpoint is the fact, alluded to earlier, that young animals are more readily and more intensely motivated by a food incentive. Such animals tend to be more active and likely to continue exploring on the first trial, even if the goal is not discovered immediately.

Furthermore, the matter of physiological health in relation to age is an important consideration. Obviously, younger animals, as a rule, are healthier and more vigorous than older ones. The latter may have faulty vision, poor muscular coordination, and similar handicaps which may exist without the experimenter's knowledge, or become apparent after the experiment has begun. It is axiomatic with experienced investigators of animal behavior that young to middle-aged animals always be selected, especially in long-term studies such as the present one. An additional reason is that the mortality rate is likely to be much lower than in an older group.

The 50 human subjects used (32 were women) were college students whose ages ranged from 18 to 21 years. They gladly volunteered to take part in this study; indeed, each subject appeared to enjoy the work somewhat as though it were a competitive game.

For our sub-hominid investigation, we were fortunate in obtaining the use of a litter of 9 small pigs through the cooperation of the Cornell Behavior Farm. These animals were of the purebred Chester White strain of domestic pig. The sex ratio in this litter was about equal, *i.e.* 5 ♀ ♀ and 4 ♂ ♂. They were exactly one month old when initially used in the maze. At that time they weighed, on the average, 14 pounds. Each animal, throughout the experiments, was strongly motivated to reach the food. Their reactions were both vigorous and noisy.

Ten dogs were employed, of which 4 were ♀ ♀ and 6 were ♂ ♂. Of the 10, 6 were purebred. Included in this purebred group were 2 dogs lent to us by the Cornell Behavior Farm, an English Bassett ♀ and a Persian Saluki ♂. The remaining purebreds were house pets borrowed from the neighborhood, a Cocker Spaniel ♂, Rat Terrier ♀, Springer Spaniel ♂, and Spitz ♀. There were 2 hybrids of purebred but different parents, a Japanese Silkhair-Rat Terrier ♂ and a Bulldog-Spaniel ♂. Finally, there were 2 mongrels, also house pets, a Beagle Hound ♂ and a Sheep Dog ♀.

All were fairly young animals, about 6 months of age, when tested in the maze. It should be noted that all these animals, especially the personal pets, had been subjected to considerable previous handling. Accordingly, there was little difficulty in habituating them to the treatment necessary in the maze situation.

Ten cats were selected. All healthy and vigorous, they were approximately 4 months of age. Of these, 6 were ♀ ♀ and 4 were ♂ ♂. All were thoroughly accustomed to being handled, as they were pets belonging to various families.

Ten purebred young chickens, of the Hampshire Red breed, were tested. All were hatched on the same day at a Batavia, New York, hatchery. After 6 weeks of development and careful taming, they were ready to run in the maze. At this age, the sexes could not be distinguished with certainty. Numbered leg-bands were left attached to the experimental chicks till they developed further, and then it was determined that 6 of them were ♀ ♀, while the remaining 4 were ♂ ♂.

Because of the vast amount of maze work that has been done with the white rat, it was thought that the study would be incomplete without this animal. Accordingly, 20 vigorous specimens were selected to round out the comparison. All were from the Yale strain. Because of our desire to use young rats of high motivation, animals were selected whose ages ranged from 150 to 200 days, the average age being about 180 days. All were ♂ ♂, the ♀ ♀ having been deliberately omitted because of the well-known fact that the estrus cycle in the rat frequently interferes with the normal course of the maze-learning performance.

Further, to round out the work, and to obtain at least an indication of the trend of results in their cases, single ısolated examples of two additional animal forms were added to the list. These animals were a young ♂ goat of mixed breed and a ♀ New Zealand white rabbit, both about 2 months of age.

A total of 42 chelonians (turtles and tortoises* of 4 different species) were used in this study. The number of specimens of each species was as follows: 27 California Desert Tortoises (*Gopherus agassizii*, Fig. 2) from the Mojave Desert, 6 Troost Turtles of Louisiana (*Pseudemys scripta troostii*), 4 Pacific Pond Turtles (*Clemmys marmorata*), and 5 New Jersey Common Box Tortoises (*Terrapene carolina carolina*). Two species are not included in the main body of the tables to be presented later, because there were too few in each group. They were 2 specimens of the Eastern Painted Turtle (*Chrysomys picta picta),* and one Common Map Turtle of Louisiana (*Graptemys geographica*). It might be of interest to mention that *Pseudemys* is the same species as the little green turtle, commonly sold in pet shops in the United States.

The exact age of each of the chelonian species was, of course, impossible to determine. Using size as a criterion, however, we selected fairly small animals which were presumably young. The single Map Turtle, 3 specimens of the Desert Tortoise (Fig. 3), 4 of the Troost Turtles, and 1 of the Pacific Pond Turtles were "baby turtles," only a few months old. They were very active, and strongly motivated by food. Baby turtles of all chelonian species are approximately two inches long. The total of 45 reptile subjects averaged around five inches in length or less, a very suitable size for the maze.† Although sex is difficult to determine in chelonians, in all our species we judged that about half of

---

* It may be pointed out that the terms "turtle" and "tortoise" are distinguished on the basis of the habitat of the animals to which they refer. "Turtle" is commonly applied to those chelonians which inhabit water for the most part, while the word "tortoise" generally refers to the land-dwelling chelonians.

† Because of the primary interest in the reptile class, the maze originally was built specifically for chelonians. Other animals were later tested in order to give a clearer perspective on the level of reptilian performance.

the turtles were ♀ and half were ♂, the judgment being based upon certain fairly definite rules of physical dimorphism.

Thus, over a period of three years of work with the Arrow Maze, a total of 156 animals of the three classes were employed.

Because of the differential speed of locomotion of the various animal forms, a time limit per maze trial was imposed upon each. This limit was consonant with the average speed of movement of the animal type in question. The turtles, which all possessed approximately the same speed, despite age and size differences, were afforded a full half-hour in which to complete a trial run. Preliminary experimentation with a few Desert Tortoises proved that this length of time was quite sufficient, even for primary trials, where progress was very slow and errors were many.

On the basis of this half-hour limit, the temporal restrictions for the other animals were determined. Since the treatment for man was necessarily different, and since the hominid subjects employed a wire-maze replica of the larger floor maze, man was omitted from the table of time limits (see Table I, below). Speed tests were made on about 5 animals of each species. The average speeds in Table I were deter-

Table I

Time Limit per Trial for Each Animal

Class of Animals	Speed in Yards per Minute	Time Limit
Reptiles		
Chelonians	5 yd./min.	30 min.
Birds		
Chicken	36.7 " "	4.1 "
Mammals		
Pig	29.2 " "	5.1 "
Rat	33.5 " "	4.5 "
Rabbit	35 " "	4.3 "
Cat	46.2 " "	3.2 "
Goat	80.4 " "	1.9 "
Dog	116 " "	1.3 "

Fig. 3a. S-1, a 2.5" baby Desert Tortoise. At the age of 110 days, when this photograph was taken, the tortoise already had 3 growth rings and weighed 50 grams.

Fig. 3b. Another print from the same negative, showing the baby California Desert Tortoise, 2.5" long, alongside an inch ruler.

mined in each case by running representative animals in a straightaway between two long boards, at the end of which food was placed as an incentive. In other words, we tested "motivated speed." This approximates maze conditions, but removes the element of time lost by the animals in turning corners, in exploring, and in changing direction or back-tracking, and similar deviations. In a word, this indicates the normal speed of locomotion of each group of animals when moving in a straight line toward food, without inter-fering factors.

Since, at present, there exists no exact means of measur-ing the amount of motivation of an animal in a maze, con-trol of this factor can be obtained only by creating con-ditions of optimal and maximal motivation. This was done in the case of all our animals by feeding each his entire allotment of food in the maze itself.* The quantity of food given was kept at a minimum in order to produce a con-siderable degree of hunger. Thus all subjects had an approx-imately equal motivation.

In order to take into account the differential capacity for food of each subject, it was obviously necessary to limit the number of trials for each animal and also the amount of food present at the goal for each trial, so that no animal would become satiated before the termination of a given test series. This was considered a better procedure than to require, arbitrarily, that a certain number of trials be com-pleted in each test period. The results seem to justify the use of this physiological criterion, which is based upon close ob-servation of behavior and experience in dealing with the animals.

Certain obvious behavioral clues indicate when suffi-cient trials for a particular animal have been given. Typical behavioral manifestations are noticeable in animals that

---

* Restricting feeding to times when the animal is in the maze has another advantage, especially with an animal that may be timid at first. It is assumed from its behavioral manifestations, that the animal soon learns to associate maze time with feeding time and therefore to "look forward" to being in the maze rather than "dreading" this occasion. This improves cooperation, and handling is less difficult.

approach satiation, and are losing optimal motivation. The white rat ceases to make a wild dash for the goal, but continually stops to clean his fur, face, and vibrissae with paws and tongue. This behavior ordinarily typifies what appears to be some sort of "frustrated" condition of the animal. Finding that food is no longer present at a former goal, active searching results, which is interrupted from time to time by the preening activity, in spite of the apparently greater importance, at the moment, of satisfying the hunger drive. On the other hand, when this type of behavior occurs near the end of a maze-learning session, it may not represent "frustration" at all. Rather, it may be a simple change of activity, affording a chance for a rest.

The chicken has its own peculiar and typical activity when motivation is decreasing. This has been observed time and again, but never during the *beginning* of the daily trials. In this work we have found that chickens should be maintained in cages where food is unavailable in order to produce optimal motivation at the time of the daily trials. But even in the cages they get some food, since they are frequently observed to catch flies and other insects in the vicinity. Once the chick is in the maze, assuming that it has had some previous experience in the situation, flies are generally disregarded, and the chick actively hunts for the scratch-feed mixture of corn, oats, and other grains, which is used as the incentive.

After a series of trials, the behavior of the bird changes very suddenly from directed movement toward the goal to aimless wandering. This is the sign for immediate removal from the maze. If allowed to remain there, the chick will make a great many errors, thus disrupting a previously perfect record. It will enter *all* the alleys in any order, and begin to chase and catch flies. Parenthetically, we may point out that the fly-catching behavior may be more than a diversion for the animals. It may be the result of a desire for a temporary change of diet. In fact, it was often noticed that, after displaying this type of performance for a while, the chicks would start directly for the goal again, only to leave the scratch feed a few moments later to hunt flies anew. Persons observing animals on a farm will have noticed that various animals are apt to turn from one type of food to another, only to return again to the original food, which meanwhile appears to have regained its appeal.

The longer we observed the behavior of chickens, the more we realized how essentially adaptable is their behavior. This well-developed ability to change suddenly from one response to another partly may account for the fact that their learning ability is remarkably high. As in the case of the dogs, cats, and pigs, the chicks learned to go consistently to a new goal, very quickly acquiring an avoidance of the previous objective. On the other hand, a white rat for a long time may continuously enter the previous goal, before reaching the correct one.

The pig, weary of running the maze, may make a flying leap to escape over the walls. The dog or cat may try to climb over or jump out in a similar fashion. But more often, after training, the latter animals simply sit in a corner to lick their fur or take a nap, as if the maze were inescapable and the animal confined in a cage. On the other hand, the dog or cat may seem to grow attached to the maze enclosure. After the completion of the daily trials, it may jump back into the maze and lie down as if to stay for the night. The animal attempts to adopt the enclosure as some sort of new home.* This behavior is probably mostly conditioned by the food. To remain in the maze would mean to be well-situated when food was next placed there.

Reactions similar to boredom were found in all the animals. If the subject, in the course of the maze-learning performance, reached the goal correctly but did not eat the food, he was removed and no further trials were given. Any increase in random, nondirective behavior caused disqualification for the time being. Special procedure was instituted for the faster animals, such as the dog, cat, and pig, so that no animal could finish the 10 correct trials for a particular goal in a single session. Such learning was delayed by distributing

---

* Such behavior on the part of the animal cannot, of course, be tolerated, for obvious reasons.

it over 3 learning periods, although not necessarily over 3 days. This tended to lessen the handicap that lower animals, such as the turtles, might otherwise have, due to their slower speed of learning. The *minimum* time permitted between any two series of trials for any animal was one hour. The maximum interval between test trial periods was about 24 hours, the length of the interval in all cases being a function of practical expediency, the particular species in question, and its special level of motivation.

Timidity in the subjects was reduced to a minimum by permitting new animals to get acquainted with their surroundings (the experimenter, buildings, cages, etc.) for a few days prior to the beginning of the maze trials. They were subjected to enough handling to remove any fear that might be present. If an animal tended to retain some degree of timidity during the initial trials in the maze, test sessions were spaced further apart in time, and more trials were presented in each session.

A greater number of trials could be given, since motivation for food was higher due to the longer interval of starvation between trials. We did this in order to take advantage of the beneficial effect for the animal, resulting from his repeated contact with the incentive. In dealing with any especially timid animal, like the young goat, the principal objective during testing was simply to make the food a more important factor than fear. The experimental subjects were not customarily fed at other times. Hence, because of the strength of the hunger drive, this technique proved exceedingly effective in removing fear.

Since our primary interest was the study of basic learning performance *per se,* and not retention, there was no necessity, as we have implied, to limit the number of trials for each animal to a constant amount. Instead, test frequency was made a function of the amount of rest necessary for the animals between learning sessions and the degree of success with which we were able to maintain optimal health and motivation in the subjects, while at the same time keeping them undistracted and unafraid during each trial.

A word concerning the differentiation of the members

of a species, one from another, might be worthy of note here. Except where physical characteristics, such as relative size or shape, pattern or coloration of markings, and the like, were sufficiently obvious to designate each subject of the same species, numbering systems were employed. In the pig, and similarly in the white rat, an ear punch was used to mark the ears. In the case of the various dogs and cats, there was, of course, no difficulty in telling the animals apart.

The 10 chickens each wore an aluminum, numbered leg-band on the right leg. When the distinction between Desert Tortoises of the same size and similar appearance was difficult, white paint served to differentiate them. (Other investigators of chelonians might find this simple system helpful.) Because ordinary painted numbers, in time, became unreadable and finally were obliterated, the costal scutes of the tortoise were assigned numbers, according to their position on the shell of the animal. The first scute at the anterior end of the carapace on the right side was designated as scute #1. Tortoise #1 of a particular size-group would have the first and tortoise #2 the second right costal scute painted white, and so on.

In a few months the paint tended to wear off through abrasion with other objects; however, as long as any trace of the color remained, there was no chance of ambiguity, because its location on the shell remained visible. A painted *number*, alone, would not be sufficient. Since chelonians are usually black, brown, or green in color, white as a contrasting marker showed up best.

As for control of sensory clues, none at all was attempted, and deliberately so. Food could easily have been distributed around the outside of the maze in order to equalize the presence of odors in different regions. Other controls might have been instituted for the other sense departments. But our original intention was to simulate, as closely as possible, a real-life situation.

As an example, we have an animal, healthy and physically fit, possessed of all its normal sensory equipment and the physiological mechanisms for acting within its environment. On the floor is an enclosure in which food is concealed.

How long will it take for the animal to find the food, and how many errors will it make while hunting for it? Any clues that the animal may perceive and make use of, in its quest for food, are to its benefit, provided such stimuli are not misinterpreted. Clues or local signs for all the species were probably numerous and varied. Different animals function according to their particular psychobiological make-up, and their place on the evolutionary scale. It is this level of ability —of the animal as a whole—in which we are especially interested in the present study.

It may well be that the various animal forms used in our maze markedly differ in their ability to make use of different sensory clues, and this may be a factor of prime importance in a comparative study of this sort. However, the environmental signs, whatever they were, remained the same for each animal.

In closing the present discussion of method, we should not omit the mention of our choice of appropriate incentives for the various animals. The efficacy of the reward in a learning problem, obviously, has an important and direct bearing on the strength of motivation in the subjects.

For human subjects, as has been previously stated, the incentive was a verbal one. The person was informed of his success in reaching the goal, and encouraged to repeat this performance.

In the case of the pig, a mixture of bran, calf meal, and skim milk was employed. The pigs preferred their food very wet (*i.e.* with plenty of skim milk), because of the summer heat, and also since, at the age of one month, they had not yet been completely weaned. Keeping the food so moist, in order to satisfy the animals, added more work to the testing procedure. Because the ravenous animals scattered their food, the maze partitions had to be frequently washed and scrubbed.

For both the dog and cat, raw ground beef or canned meat was provided. The experimental chicks were fed regular scratch feed. As an incentive for the white rats, calf meal was employed. This food was moistened with water, because of the animal's preference for wet food. In the brief time that the rat was allowed to remain at the goal in each trial, the rodent would eat more of the calf meal if it was moist than if it was dry.

The rabbit showed a preference for freshly picked clover and grass, and also for carrot cubes, carrot greens, and the like. The rabbit, like many other animals, tires of a one-item menu. Therefore, the experimenter habitually provided a variety of cut, raw vegetables of the kind just listed. The same type of food assortment was found to make the most effective incentive for the young goat. Oats, which were tried at first with this animal, met with little success. (Mature goats, on the other hand, seem to prefer oats and other grains.)

As for the various chelonian species, all the water turtles and the Box Tortoises favored raw beef ground up for easy swallowing. Since water turtles prefer to eat under water, a low glass dish of fresh cold water was provided for these animals at the site of the goal in the maze. The dish was not visible, either from the front of the maze or from the entrance to the correct alley. A small glass block served as a stand to hold the small pinch of beef that was used as the incentive in each trial. The glass block was within the water dish on the nearer side so that the animal could readily reach it and then climb into the dish to eat, if he so desired. This habit of eating with the head submerged has probably developed in water turtles, because the natural propensity for withdrawing to their customary habitat leads them to spend most of their time under water, and consequently to satisfy the main part of their nutritional needs in the same medium.*

---

* We have observed *Clemmys marmorata* (Pacific Pond Turtles of California, Washington, and Oregon) in a large tank disregard tempting bits of meat left on a rock at the water's edge, but immediately pounce upon it when the meat was placed in the water and allowed to sink to the bottom. Apparently, the water species of chelonians find it simpler and more practical to tear their food apart under water by means of their sharp jaws and needle-like claws, since the water tends to soften the food. They also, apparently, find greater security in the concealment that this medium often affords, and rather than feed in full view on land, they will, if possible, drag their food into the water to eat.

The Desert Tortoise was given an entirely different kind of food. Although it takes time to get this tortoise accustomed to eating food which it does not ordinarily eat in its natural habitat, it seemed to relish lettuce. The fact that such a succulent, leafy plant is not to be found on desert soil, and therefore is strange to the taste of the animal, seems to be the only reason why the species must become habituated to it over a brief period of time. However, it was interesting to note that, once it has eaten this food a few times, it no longer prefers ordinary desert plants. The reason for this increasing fondness for lettuce seems to be that the vegetable is readily torn or cut apart by the reptile's hard, horny jaws and the thick, blunt nails of the forelegs. A second reason, not less important, seems to be the large water content of lettuce.*

In maze work, most investigators allow time before the regular trials for an habituation period for each animal, dur-

* As a consequence of previous behavior habits, developed while still in their natural habitat, laboratory animals of this species preferred leafy plants of high water content, whenever such were available. This was true even though dishes of water were normally on hand. Captive Desert Tortoises will drink water from a container at certain not too frequent intervals of time, but particularly after they have been brought from the desert at the end of a collecting trip. At such a time, we have observed specimens drinking for many minutes in the laboratory at CalTech, with hardly a pause for adequate respiration. Despite these facts, namely, that in the laboratory the animals could find sufficient water and were seen to drink periodically from the dishes, they preferred lettuce, and the like, when it was liberally sprinkled with water. This was in addition, of course, to the already high water content of the cells of this plant. Leafy vegetables that had dried up overnight would not be touched unless moisture was artificially restored. Furthermore, cabbage, which has a very dry leaf, tougher than lettuce, is more difficult for the animals to break up and eat, and as a consequence the tortoises avoided it as long as there was also some lettuce in the vicinity. Other vegetables that they ate while under our care, but which seemed a great deal less desirable to them than lettuce, included the avocado, broccoli, grass and clover, cauliflower, celery, carrot and turnip-tops, parsley, pea pods, potato skins, and tomato. Among the fruits observed to be eaten were apple, cantaloup and watermelon (much moisture!), grapes, orange and tangerine pulp and skins, and finally pear. Miscellaneous items of a more unusual nature could be added to the list, such as the very moist cornmeal-molasses-agar medium employed in raising fruit-flies (Drosophila); also hazelnuts and cashew nuts when broken into small pieces for them, swordfish, twigs, and finally paper (newsprint, paper towelling, etc.), especially when moistened with food juices.

ing which time no food is present in the maze. The animal
is permitted to roam at will through the apparatus. This procedure, however, was not followed in the present work. From
the beginning, food was present in the Arrow Maze. This
was done because we wished to simulate, as far as possible,
natural conditions, similar to those which the animal might
be apt to face outdoors. Therefore, the primary trials in our
work were, generally, long in duration, during which time
the animal often explored many or all of the alleys. Because
the animal in the first trial obviously did not know that food
was available in the maze until he had found it for the first
time, this trial was often spent in aimless wandering. As a
result, the food was sometimes not discovered within the
time limit. This, however, was exceptional, although, as
would be expected, there were more such unsuccessful trials
with the reptiles than with the birds or mammals.

III. QUALITATIVE RESULTS

OUR PURPOSE IN THIS SECTION IS TO DESCRIBE QUALITATIVELY, from the comparative point of view, the behavior of each of the animal forms.

What does an animal do in the maze in the process of finding its way to the goal? The human subjects, rating the highest performance score, were quick initial learners. However, they proved slower at relearning (with each change of the location of the goal) than we had anticipated. With the first experience with the maze, the typical behavior of all human subjects was a wandering search through the labyrinth in order to grasp its pattern by touch. In the verbal directions, they were never told that it *was* a maze, since the turtles and other animals were not, of course, "instructed" in this manner.

After the goal was discovered for the first time, the next bit of behavior which we observed was an attempt to repeat the latter part of the pathway just prior to reaching the goal. This route was often very roundabout. It usually took a considerable time before short cuts were attempted or accidentally discovered, the tendency being to continue to use longer routes which had previously led to the goal. The change in the goal's location was always a shock to the subject, in that any degree of confidence that he had built up concerning his success in this problem was suddenly dissipated. That which had been correct was now incorrect. Something was fundamentally "wrong."

"There must be a catch to this," the subjects often said, or "You must have changed the goal!" Then each subject altered his procedure by trying other pathways. However, this temporary state of confusion sometimes lasted for a number of trials. Of course, once it was realized that location of the goal had been actually altered, a further change of the goal site did not elicit the same excitement nor did it cause the same delay. One cannot avoid pointing out the similarity of this to that noticed in lower animals, in which considerable "surprise," excitement, and often irritation was exhibited when the goal had been changed.

We shall next deal with the domestic pig, since it ranked second in our experimental series. It is no surprise that the pig should rank so high, as Liddell, James, Anderson[11] and Yerkes[14] have already indicated. The fact that the pig was a swift learner worked as both an advantage and a disadvantage for the animal. It could learn a stereotyped habit in a short while with very few errors, but it appeared to forget what it had learned with almost the same speed. In other words, each trial series was reacted to as an isolated situation to which the animal must adapt, with apparently little utilization of, or benefit from, past experience. Pigs that had run a correct pathway a number of times would tend to go elsewhere on the first trial of the following day.

This evidence of poor retention may be due simply to the animal's erratic behavior, its overabundance of energy, and the great amount of motivation it possesses when beginning the day's trials. Because of the high rate of energy consumption and, consequently, the large amount of food that it eats, trials were run at least twice a day, usually in the morning and early evening. Much more food was permitted in each trial as the reward than in the case of an animal of smaller capacity such as the dog. Because of the brief time intervals and the change of goal location from time to time, the Arrow Maze is not essentially a test of retention. Whatever little degree of retention the pig possessed was sufficient for the maze situation herein utilized, since many trials were given in one session.

During and just prior to the testing period, each pig was kept in a separate cage. This permitted quick location of the desired animal, and decreased fear reactions when removing or replacing the animal in his cage. (When pigs are left together in a single cage, removal of one elicits wild screams and "tantrum behavior" from the rest.) But the most important factor was that such isolation made the animal accustomed to being alone and separated from the rest of the litter. When placed by itself in the maze enclosure, there was less tendency for it to show evidence of fear or to become uncooperative. For animals that might attempt to escape from the maze during the first trials, such as the dog, cat, and pig, the outer walls were raised to about twice their normal height through the use of additional boards. This tended to discourage such behavior.

The pig, after being placed in the maze, at first would generally make a great leap for the nearest wall in an attempt to surmount it. After a few such fruitless but vigorous collisions with the wall, it would change its course of behavior from one of attempting to escape to one of exploring its new environment. Desire to scale the walls was replaced by a new viewpoint of interest and excitement when food was first discovered within the enclosure. Thenceforth, little further trouble was experienced, except in handling the pig each time it was removed from the food in readiness for a new trial. But this reaction, apparently, was evidence of the high motivation present in the animal, fear being no longer a factor by that time.

Typical of all nine of the pigs, while running the maze, was the high rate of speed with which they travelled through the alleys, whether in the first trial or in one of the later series. Because of the pigs' rapid learning, the trials often had to be terminated before complete satiation, as explained previously (to avoid running too much of the maze routine in a single session). However, the pigs received extra food after the evening session if they seemed to want it sufficiently. (This would carry them through until the trials of the following morning.)

The headlong catapulting through the maze resulted in often-repeated lateral collisions with the partitions, which only served to make the pig run faster, all the while rending the air with staccato, high-pitched squeals.* But continued close observation clearly demonstrated that this behavior was what would be called in hominids "aggressive response to frustrating circumstances" rather than evidence of fear. If fear was present in the first trials, it was indicated by loud squeals and attempts to scale the walls. The little shrill squeals in later trials were, apparently, indicative of excitement, not fear, and may be considered analogous to the "peeps" of baby chicks while running down the alleys in search of food in the same rapid fashion.

The dog ranks next to the pig in our series. In this study, it was found that the dog learns considerably more rapidly than the cat, makes fewer errors, but lacks the almost immediate adaptive changes of behavior noticed in the pig. The dog, apparently, has superior retention as compared with the pig or cat, and this serves him well. Once he began to learn the correct alley, he did not readily forget it. But this advantage is not sufficient to warrant ranking the dog above the pig, for the latter animal learns with such lightning speed. If the Arrow Maze tested retention as well as learning *per se*, the dog would probably rank more nearly on a par with the pig in our list.

---

* Some notes in regard to the squealing response in pigs, written during our work with the litter of nine in the maze, should prove explanatory and also of interest at this point. "The pig," we recorded, "soon learns not to resist when picked up in preparation for the next trial, and also learns not to squeal. The squeal, however, must not be mistaken as merely a sign of fear alone in the pig. A pig will squeal—just as a dog will bark—in a number of widely different circumstances. He has a particular squeal when he is fighting his way to a coveted dish of food, when nursing or feeding hungrily and also when fighting with other members of the litter (ear biting and scratching till the blood flows being common), when chased, or dropped from a height, or otherwise frightened or excited. There are squeals induced when the pig is removed from, or returned to, the company of other pigs. Obvious differences are apparent in these sounds. Real fright is evidenced by long, loud, piercing squeals, while pleasurable excitement during eating, for instance, is indicated by a series of short squeals and grunts which are fairly soft."

As an additional experiment, a true test of retention was executed with one of the dogs, the Bulldog-Spaniel ♂. This puppy, at two months of age, completed the 4 alleys of the maze with a total of 61 errors (as defined later, see IV. Quantitative Results). One month later, the puppy was permitted to run the maze routine again exactly as before. A decided improvement in speed of learning was noted. The number of errors was reduced from 61 to 23, or approximately to a third of the former number. Remembrance of the serial order of alleys to be learned (3-2-4-1) would probably be difficult for any animal, and there was no evidence of such retention in this dog. However, practice and experience with the general maze routine was apparently not forgotten, and therefore it was possible for relearning to be much more rapid. The criterion for each alley was satisfied in a more efficient and business-like manner.

The final test, one month later, lowered the preceding month's score to one-fourth of its value. Only 6 errors were committed. Thus, even with the distributed practice afforded by sets of trials a month apart, the results indicated marked improvement. From this we would suspect that retention of such a maze routine would be effective over a period of many months in the dog.

The typical reaction of the dog, when it was unable to locate the food immediately in the first trial, was either to stop further wandering and lie down on the floor of the maze or to attempt to jump out. Trouble of this nature was often experienced in the first few trials with the dog. Other animals, particularly rodents such as the rat and rabbit, tend to begin exploring any strange new place immediately. But the dog is apparently so dependent upon man for cues to activity, for orders and direction, that it may just sit and look about as though awaiting its cue from the experimenter before going into action. Leaving the room entirely, and observing the dog's behavior through a one-way window, was unsuccessful. The dogs almost always disregarded the maze situation and went to sleep. The stimulus of the presence of the experimenter in the proximity of the maze was necessary in order to keep the animal in a state of activity and to affect its cooperation in the maze routine.

The dog usually discovered that the maze contained food in the first or second trial. Once the food was found, the animal's interest and attention, generally speaking, passed from the experimenter to the maze situation. No longer was the box just an enclosure; now it was an exciting place where food might be found. The dogs then appeared to take the maze routine as a sort of game, like fetching a ball after it is tossed, and the animals eagerly awaited the signal to enter the maze for each successive trial.*

The writer has been convinced by particular behavioral manifestations noticed in the dogs in the Arrow Maze, that they apparently depended more upon visual than upon olfactory cues. No animal, while within this maze, can be more than one or two yards from the location of the food incentive (in any of the four goals), and this distance is a short one for odors to travel. Since there was no roof of any sort to the maze, there was nothing to obstruct the radiation of the odors from the food. We have already mentioned that the dog might cease exploring in the very first trial, and lie down to sleep. This behavior is difficult to explain, if we are to believe that the dog is making the best use of his olfactory sensitivity. Furthermore, we have repeatedly observed dogs, while learning the first alley or a new one, to enter the correct pathway and proceed along it almost to the goal, then stop, turn around and come out again. In turning, at times they had to move the head directly over the meat that had been placed in the goal site.

The speed with which the dog runs in and out of alleys in its frantic search would suffice to explain why it would not see a small quantity of food. But this speed would not be excessive enough to prevent the marked olfactory stimuli of fresh, moist meat from reaching the dog's nostrils. The writer is in agreement with the evidence of past observations

---

* This is also the case with dogs in conditioning experiments. We are informed that the animals, on becoming accustomed to the routine, are eager to take part in the experiments.

that canine vision is color-blind and vague, while olfactory sensitivity is very keen. But the domesticated dog, in such a problem as the maze presents, apparently does not use its olfactory sense to its own best advantage.

The young ♂ goat (only a single specimen was employed) showed a maze performance about on a level with that of the rat and the chick, but a good deal lower than the dog. The goat was superior to the cat. Stubbornness, resistance to handling, frustration in seeking food and some inevitable fear of the maze situation tended to lower the score of the goat. But with great patience on the part of the experimenter, plus starving the animal for a period prior to the test, it was successfully tested. It proved a fairly rapid learner after the preliminary trials were completed. Errors at first were numerous, but once the goat grew accustomed to the maze routine the learning was faster, and the animal became quite adept at changing the direction of its search for each new goal.

In the initial phase, the first reaction within the strange maze enclosure was to stamp the hoofs, paw the floor, and repeatedly attempt to bolt over the wall. Since the time for each trial was restricted to the actual "running time" for all animals (i.e. only that time employed in actual searching for food or exploring pathways), such behavior of the goat, described above, did not unfairly prolong the number of trials.

The finding of food within the maze, as in the case of the other animals, served to make the goat more cooperative. It even began to show impatience at the delay between each successive trial (while the experimenter was completing the act of recording time and pathways travelled), and would immediately attempt to enter the maze again. An assistant would be necessary to restrain the animal until the "timer" had been reset to zero, and more food placed at the goal in readiness for the following trial.

Yerkes,[14] as already stated in I. In Retrospect, employed the pig, crow, and white rat as subjects, and found that the crow ranked second to the pig in learning ability or speed and level of performance. In our present study, another representative of the Aves class, the chicken, likewise assumed a high place in the learning scale, ranking just below the dog, and approximately on a par with the rat. (The chick scored a higher PQ than the rat, but the rat rated a TQ and AQ above that of the chick. The average Q-score for both forms was exactly the same, 31.9. For a definition of these symbols, IV. Quantitative Results should be consulted.)

The high ranking of the chicken in our learning scale was not so curious when the chick's behavior was analyzed. It was found to be somewhat akin to the pig in behavioral manifestations while in the maze situation. Like the pig, it was erratic, fast in locomotion, and quick in learning a stereotyped response. The chick was likewise quick to alter this pattern in favor of a new one when the incentive was transferred to a different location. As in the case of the pig, the chick demonstrated poor retention, in fact, the worst of any of the animals studied. (The reptile class, for instance, did far better in this regard.) The chick developed and discarded stereotyped response patterns with equal ease and rapidity, and it was only a little slower in reducing errors than the pig.

Trial-and-error learning for the chick was not a long-drawn-out process. Instead, after the incentive had been changed to a new goal, the chick would often run to each of the other alleys, one after another in rapid succession, until the food was located. This behavior, which was observed a number of times in all of the chicks, would seem to indicate that the birds expected to find food elsewhere in the maze. There was no hesitation at any time, nor was a moment taken for rest or other pursuits, as long as motivation was maintained. However, the dog possessed an advantage over both pig and chick, in that it displayed less of an erratic type of behavior, being apparently slower, more deliberate and selective in its activities.

A decrease in motivation, as already suggested, resulted in a radical change in behavior. The chick turned from hunting the location of the dish of corn to chasing flies.

Haphazard, rather than directive exploring about the maze was adopted with a consequent multiplicity of errors. Other typical behavior that the bird displayed, if permitted to remain in the maze too long, was the flight to the top of the maze walls from which it would either jump down and escape, or remain perched on the board, preening its feathers. Boredom, rather than fear, was very likely the chief reason for escape from the maze, since the animals had grown extremely tame after more than a month of watchful care and handling.

As is only too well-known to workers in this field, the white rat is a more cooperative laboratory subject than, for example, the pig and chicken. But the results obtained with the albino rat were poorer than expected. Nevertheless, it was quite a surprise to discover the rat's superiority over the cat in the Arrow Maze. The author believes that the white rat has the highest level of performance of rodents in general, at least of those more commonly employed in animal laboratories. The score of the single rabbit that we tested was about four points lower that the average rat score, but still above the cat. Furthermore, Riess[8] has shown that the guinea pig (cavy), another member of the rodent group, was unable to learn to step on two metal plates in succession on the floor of a problem box in order to obtain food. Rats in the same apparatus, on the other hand, were successful in learning this problem.

The experimental rats which the writer used were motivated to an optimal degree by feeding the animals only during the daily trials. Whatever part of the food allowance remained in the dishes was given to them at the close of the evening trials. Because normal *ad lib* feeding was not permitted between test series, the animals tended to race through the alleys of the maze in their search for food. This speed of travelling is typical of rats in all learning situations (Multiple-T Maze, Maier Reasoning Apparatus, Lashley Maze, and the like) where distance of any degree exists between the starting compartment of the apparatus and the goal. It proved more of a handicap than a help to our rats, as their headlong dashing produced a great many errors.

Although the rat had the same rank order of learning ability as the chick, there was a difference in the degree of stereotyped response in the two animals. The chick, as we have pointed out, varied its behavior quickly, adjusting without delay to a change in the total situation. The rat, on the other hand, piled up errors by its persistence in re-entering the former alleys, which no longer led to the food. It is interesting to note that in the rat, in which behavior is clearly more stereotyped, individual differences of performance level are more marked and noticeable than in the higher animals, such as the dog or chick. Phylogenetically, we would expect the rat, a mammal, to be superior to the chick, a bird, and to be less stereotyped in behavior. But this common concept in regard to the relation between birds and mammals apparently has its exceptions. This relation was also brought out in Yerkes' work,[14] where it will be remembered that the crow ranked above the rat.

The rat, as well as the cat which will be discussed presently, was handicapped by an insufficiently adaptable form of behavior when the goal situation changed. The rat, set to learn a *single* objective (the shortest path to the food chamber in a Lashley Maze, for example), could learn fairly rapidly. After perfection of its newly acquired habit, it could retain this behavior for a matter of months without practice. It was the change in the experimental conditions that disturbed the rat's equilibrium. His learned routine was upset and there appeared a type of "conflict" between the old and the new, between the first goal and the second one. Accordingly, his behavior became more erratic and less organized. Only with difficulty did the rat learn to attempt a new pattern of action. It persisted in the old routine, multiplying errors under conditions in which the chickens readily perfected a new pattern of adaptive behavior.

It is interesting to note that when the rat was first put into the maze, it persisted in a tendency to hug the outer walls of the enclosure during the first trials. After the animal became more familiar with the maze, this behavior completely disappeared, and it henceforth ran along the center of the pathways. This tendency had another effect during the first trial: it diverted the animal toward the outer alleys (1 and 4), so that reaching alley #3 (the first goal) was momentarily delayed. It is the natural behavior of rats to follow closely walls of any sort in a strange place, but the particular behavior described probably had a further reason. This was the attempt during the primary exploration of the maze to find an opening in the outside walls through which to make an escape. This tendency, when present, was merely a temporary manifestation which disappeared as soon as food was discovered in the maze.

As with the dog, the sense of smell seems to offer little aid to the rat in the maze. We have observed on more than one occasion that a rat may stumble across the food dish at the goal site, during its preliminary exploration of the maze, without noticing the food at all. In such cases, despite the high motivation of the rat for food, it did not immediately turn back in its tracks to follow the scent. Only later, as a result of an accidental re-entry into the correct alley, would the food be discovered. Once the food was found, there was no hesitation in eating it and, in later trials, it was no longer overlooked.

In hunting a new goal, the rat often runs up each alley *in turn* until he finds it. This is a logical system, perhaps, except for the fact that this animal, unlike the chicken, was likely to re-enter the *same* alley a number of times in direct succession, as if still uncertain concerning the removal of the food to a new location. The animal's behavior seemed to be characterized by much aimless running about which appeared to have little meaning in terms of accomplishment.

Just below the rat and the chick in learning performance came the single rabbit specimen. Although it attained a score higher than the average cat-value, the cat was a better maze subject. The rabbit, whose main protection in nature is speed of escape and blending coloration, demanded a great deal more patience in handling because of its natural timidity. It made a great many errors during the first trials while learning a new goal but, once it started correctly going to the food in each successive trial, the odds were in favor of its continuing success. The cat on the other hand, is more likely to break a successful run of trials. Like other rodents, the rabbit develops a stereotyped response, and thereafter learns a new goal location only with difficulty.

The cat was discovered to be a slow learner. At the same time, it lacked the ability to "forget" or discard a previously learned response, when this was a necessary factor in learning a new goal. In the Arrow Maze, it will be remembered that disregarding one goal (or alley) was necessary before the next goal could be satisfactorily learned. Becoming overstereotyped in a single pattern of behavior, the cat wastes much time, amassing considerable errors, while trying to erase this pattern and replace it with the new one.

The difference between the cat and dog, in performance level in the Arrow Maze, is certainly not a mere function of differential motivation. Both were normally fed only during the maze trials. The cat was as highly motivated as the dog, apparently, since considerable vocalizing resulted when it could not locate the food. The cat would sit in the previously correct alley, and begin to mew loudly. The dog, on the other hand, would whine a moment or so, but normally wasted little time in "complaining" in this manner. Instead, usually it immediately ran to other alleys in search of food.

An interesting bit of behavior, often noticed in cats and dogs and many of the other forms, is that of returning to the old alley after food had just been discovered in the new goal, as if the animal expected or at least hoped to find the food also in the old goal. This phenomenon may partly be due to older kinesthetic habits that had not yet disintegrated in the new situation. Another possibility is that a lack of clarity existed in the total situation as perceived by the animal. Because the new behavioral pattern had not yet been clearly defined in the animal, the above confusion resulted.

We now turn to the remaining species in our study, which together make up the chelonian group. The experimenter omitted the Eastern Painted Turtle, *Chryse-*

mys picta picta, from the main body of the tables in the Quantitative Results (to be discussed later) because only two specimens were employed. Nevertheless, it is noteworthy to point out that these two animals ranked higher than the goat, rat, chick, rabbit, and cat! On the other hand, the remaining five species of turtles ranked about as generally expected, namely, at the bottom of our rank order list.

The Painted Turtle is probably a very exceptional member of the chelonian group. We would be more skeptical if only one specimen had been tested, but when two ranked so high, it was more difficult to disregard such atypical results.

This species, however, does not differ from the other chelonians in regard to the presence of stereotyped behavior. Nevertheless, there was a marked difference in their performance which would seem to explain, at least in part, their high score in the Arrow Maze. This difference, which sets them apart in such an unexpected fashion, is that they were quick to learn a new habit and to drop the old one. In this regard, they are similar to the chicken. The Painted Turtles required a fairly long time to learn alley #3, just as did all the turtles that we studied. But when the food was no longer to be found in alley #3, they did not lose as many trials as other chelonians in learning to direct their movements toward alley #2. These were very active water turtles; perhaps this species is more readily motivated than other water turtles that we used, such as *Pseudemys* or *Graptemys.*

On the other hand, possibly kinesthesis in this animal was subordinated to the other senses to a degree unlike that in the other species tested. Discrimination between different alleys, due to a keener awareness of variations in direction, position, and shape of the partitions, olfactory acuity, or superior retention of performance between individual trials may have been involved. Future research of a more specific and intricate nature will be necessary, before the real reason is ascertained.

The Painted Turtle and other chelonians have one advantage over animals such as the rat. Since the turtle is a slow-moving animal, it possesses a longer time limit in accordance with the procedure employed in the present study. Consequently, there is more time for selection of appropriate turns or approaches, for reorganization of bodily movement and adjustment to environmental change. The rat is a fast worker, racing rather than walking through the pathways. Such headlong response to the maze situation tends to multiply errors, which otherwise might have been avoided. The turtle, on the other hand, with its low reserve of energy, has a limited speed and therefore has a chance to make a better adjustment.

In general, the remaining members of the reptile group ranked somewhat close together, although there were certain obvious differences in the performance of the water and land species. The water species were all superior to the land forms in learning ability. The Desert Tortoise ranked above the Box Tortoise, which ranked lowest of the entire chelonian group.

It is the strong conviction of the author, after many years of observation of different species of chelonians (including those mentioned here), that the normal environment of each species greatly affects or at least closely correlates with their respective behavior and learning performance. Water species need speed to catch their live prey, and to escape from other water forms that may hunt them. The land tortoise, on the other hand, does not need to move about quickly, because it feeds upon plants. Sometimes it feeds upon dead animal matter, but rarely, if ever, upon living, moving animals. The land tortoise cannot progress with the same speed that a water species can maintain when placed on land. Apparently, the energy reserves of the two types of reptiles are quite different in magnitude.

Furthermore, the land dweller among the chelonians possesses a much harder shell than is customarily found in the water varieties, and this adequately serves as a defense mechanism against animals that would prey upon it.* Indeed, it is impossible for the land tortoise to escape from its enemies by means of locomotion, for it is too slow. A heavy weight must be borne upon short, stubby legs. It therefore uses its chief defense, namely, withdrawal into its hard shell.

The sluggish Desert Tortoise, native to a hot, arid climate, retains its low metabolic rate even after being transferred to a colder climate for a number of years. If circumstances are favorable, most of the day is spent in sleeping or basking in the sun. It was next to the slowest learner on our list, and yet was permitted more than enough time with which to complete each trial.

The Box Tortoise, accustomed to a colder climate, but not very much more active than the desert species, proved no better in maze performance. However, the very active water turtles with probably higher BMR† all ranked above the land tortoises. Work upon the relative metabolic status of the chelonians might shed some light upon the hypothesis of the probable relation of energy reserve to learning performance in these animals.

Except for the extraordinary Eastern Painted Turtles described above, the chelonians readily became stereotyped and habituated in their maze performance after a number of trials. They seemed to break a habit with difficulty and only after a long period of time. To their own advantage, the turtles showed excellent retention of the behavioral patterns which they adopted. This retention was superior to

---

* We have often noted the marks of what are believed to be coyote teeth, which match on both the carapace and plastron of Desert Tortoises. It takes a few years before the shell of the young tortoise has hardened sufficiently. After this process is complete, the reptile apparently can withstand the savage attacks of the coyotes, a few of which still roam the lonely stretches of the Mojave Desert under the cover of night. There is no other present-day desert animal of this size that would be large enough to inflict such marks upon the shells of these chelonians. From the fact that such dorsal and ventral imprints of teeth have been found in specimens of all sizes, including those too large to be held in the span of the jaws of the coyote, we may conclude that such deformities never leave or "grow out of" a chelonian's shell, but remain throughout life.
† Basal metabolic rate.

that displayed by the chicken or pig in our particular maze. But the turtles have more time to permit their habits to become "set," as it were. They can be induced to run only a few trials per day, before they resist further testing, and slip into a corner to sleep or scrape against the maze wall as if attempting to escape. This means that day-to-day retention is more of a necessity for the turtles than for the higher vertebrates which learn a given goal much faster. Thus we see that the chelonians as a group are slow initial learners, slow forgetters, and slow relearners.

Although similarities of behavior were apparent in animals of all classes and species tested in the Arrow Maze, there were, as would be expected, essential and characteristic class and species differences. Thus it was necessary to deal with each biological group in a scientifically cautious and specific manner in the practical situation of learning the maze problem. The steps taken in working with dogs, for example, were often inapplicable in the case of cats. Each animal form, studied during the course of the research, presented its own special problems.

In the Appendix of this report we have included a series of graphic tracings of the route taken by a typical member of each animal form in running the Arrow Maze. The pathway followed by the animal in the unmotivated* first trial is compared with that traversed in the motivated second trial.

* That is to say, not motivated by the *food* incentive, although it is assumed from behavioral observations that the animal subject in each case v...s impelled to wander through the maze by another drive, such as the desire to explore or to escape.

IV. QUANTITATIVE RESULTS

The Arrow Maze, with specific procedure as outlined under II. Method, is a test, not essentially of retention, but of learning ability, habit formation, and maintenance of a learned habit. It is also a test of the ability of an animal to forsake or forget an old behavioral pattern when a new one must be substituted.

In order to satisfy the learning criterion for each goal, the animal subject was required to enter the correct alley for 10 times in direct succession, without making any errors (*i.e.* wanderings into *other* alleys). This primary requirement tested the animal's learning speed, as measured by relative time and, more important, by the number of trials that were necessary. Retention of what had been learned was necessary from trial to trial in order to fulfill each criterion. But since the time interval between trials was so brief, except in the turtles, the required amount of retention demanded of each animal subject was very little.

The particular behavior which the animal found successful, *i.e.* which led it to food, had to be maintained for the brief space of 10 trials, as we have stated, *but no longer.* If the animal had formed fixed habits after such practice periods, it was often handicapped in the further learning routine of the maze. Such an animal was slow to adjust to a change in the location of the goal.

That the Arrow Maze is likewise a test of the ability to forget, should not be overlooked. At least, it tests the ability to *disregard* those goals which have previously contained food, but which are no longer incentive locations. The intelligent animal may not be able to eliminate entirely his past responses, which is to be expected. However, he will tend to adapt himself quickly to the revised situation by attempting to avoid consistently the kinesthetic and memorial inducements (if such be present) to re-enter the old pathways.

The primary habit patterns must be deliberately broken, and each new behavioral complex substituted. Relearning (*i.e.* learning a new goal) must function without delay if the animal is to secure a high score in the Arrow Maze.

Relearning should not take as long as learning the first alley, despite the conflict between the two goals, because of the fact that the subject now possesses the advantage of previous practice and adaptation to the maze routine. More important, the animal's primary exploratory trials in the apparatus should acquaint it, especially through its visual and other sensory mechanisms, with the general layout or pattern of the four alleys, and their relation to the entrance or starting point. The central alleys differ in pattern from the lateral alleys (as can readily be seen from the floor plan of the maze in Fig. 1), thus affording differential clues that should be readily perceived by vertebrate animals with normal vision.

Furthermore, a few trials were probably saved in learning the second alley, for by then the animal should be fully "informed" of the fact that food was to be found in the enclosure, whereas this might have remained an incidental factor to the animal during the primary trials. We may assume, in consideration of the fact that our animals were high in the biological scale, that each successive contact with the food in the maze probably strengthened their awareness or recognition of the presence of the incentive at the end of the correct pathway.*

---

* We are unwilling to agree with those psychologists who disclaim that there is any possibility of such a thing as "anticipation" (as of food) in the neutral processes of infrahominid animals. The maze subjects return to the very same place 10 or more times in succession. Is this purely mechanical (kinesthetic)? Is there no psychophysiological "expectancy" of obtaining

The scores for all species were related to the results obtained with man by a very simple formula, for which tables were devised in order to save time in figuring. For convenience, man's level of ability in the solution of the maze problem was made the standard of reference, and the resulting quantification was labeled the *Performance Quotient* or PQ.*

With man's average PQ arbitrarily set at 100, the PQ of each of the other animals on our list may be considered conveniently as a *percentage* of the learning ability of man. For example, the domestic pig of the Chester White strain, which ranks second to man on our limited list, was found to have a PQ about 50% that of man. Next to the pig came the dog with a Performance Quotient of about 40; the chick was above 30, while the rodents and other mammals that we tested formed a group having a PQ of about 25. The reptile class (the chelonians in this case) had a PQ of about 15. This provides a brief survey from a broad view of performance relationships between various animal forms in this research.

Obviously, the more trials the animal needs to satisfy the criteria in any learning situation, the more time will be required for the animal to complete the learning problem. It is customarily assumed in experiments on the learning process in animals that rapid learning implies a greater development and a more complete use of the organism's faculties, which may be quite different in various animal forms.

---

food in the same place, where it has been discovered so many times before? The various animals fulfill the requirements of the learning criteria just as man does. Is man's behavior in this regard automatic and divorced of thought processes? Where is one to draw the line? Below man? Below the pig, or the dog, or below the birds and mammals as a whole? Such argument seems foolish and futile. It seems evident from many indications (not only in this work, but also in that of earlier researchers), that the animal goes to the goal—not from mere habit alone—but because he has learned to expect satisfaction of his food needs there.

* H. C. Link, 1936,[18] has employed the letters "P.Q." to symbolize "Personality Quotient" in connection with the combined results of a battery of hominid personality tests. However, we have chosen to retain the same letters for our particular purpose, because of the terms which they fittingly represent in the present study.

Whether true or not, it is superfluous to argue the point at the present level of our knowledge of these matters. In any case, the number of trials that a given animal needed in order to solve this maze problem was considered the most significant basis upon which to work out the Performance Quotient.

In the determination of the Performance Quotient, the sum of the trials necessary for learning the complete four-alley routine of the Arrow Maze was considered the total number of "errors." This value is the P- or Performance-value of the animal, and naturally excludes the 10 successive correct trials to each alley. (The latter are obviously not errors and therefore are not included.) The average P-value of man is 14.8 (trials), the PQ being 100 as stated above. The original formula for deriving the PQ of any animal is as follows:

$$\frac{\text{P-value of man}}{\text{P-value of animal}} = \frac{\text{PQ of animal}}{\text{PQ of man}}$$

Note that one relationship is simply the *reciprocal* of the other. The obvious reason for this arrangement is to bring logic into the resultant scores; that is, a high degree of error produces a low PQ. On the other hand, a small number of errors (low P-value) results in a high Performance Quotient. It was considered desirable to have the higher PQ's represent the better performance scores in this manner.

If we now return to the above formula, we can substitute for the symbols the values of an actual case, one of the domestic pig subjects used in the maze. The P-value of man, as stated, was 14.8 (which is the average value obtained with the 50 subjects). The PQ of man is 100, given. Pig #1 made a total of 20 trial errors so that the P-value of this animal was 20. We now determine the PQ score for this particular maze subject:

$$\frac{14.8}{20} = \frac{PQ}{100}$$

Cross-multiplying, we have:

$$20 \; PQ = 1480$$
$$PQ = 1480/20 = 74$$

Thus the PQ of the first pig run in the Arrow Maze was very high, a score of 74. (This animal lost 5 trials in learning alley #3, needed 9 trials to learn alley #2, and 3 trials each for alleys #4 and #1, or a total of 20 trials.)

To simplify the above procedure, the shorter formula,

$$PQ = 1480/P$$

was employed, and tables were devised for the more common P-values. This saved the time involved in recomputation and rechecking. Given a certain P-value, one could locate in the tables the appropriate (equivalent) PQ score.*

The use of this formula had certain advantages. It related all animals to man in a quick, convenient, and easily visualized fashion. The larger PQ thus designates, logically, the superior performance rather than vice versa, as with error summation. The convenience of considering the animal's performance as a percentage of the performance level of man has already been mentioned. Important is the practical consideration that the PQ limits are permanently set between the numbers 0 and 100.† This is both a simplification and a convenience. We would suspect, for instance, that the chimpanzee, if tested in sufficient numbers in the Arrow Maze (or its equivalent of a larger size), would rank somewhere between the pig average and the average for man, probably closer to the latter (100) than to the former (50).

In order to ascertain whether PQ was truly a valid measure of relative performance in a learning situation, two

---

* These tables of P-PQ equivalents are not reproduced in this paper, because they would be valueless to another worker, unless he employed the same maze under the same conditions as herein set forth.

† Since 100 is only an average, it is quite possible for individual scores of hominids (and *possibly* even of some of the other primates?) to ascend above 100. With so many human subjects, there was, expectedly, a wide range of individual differences in man, the largest PQ score being 336.

other criteria of error were selected.* Two more quotients were invented in exactly the same manner as PQ in order to accommodate these new measures of performance.

The first of these criteria, TQ (or Minimum Trial Quotient) is simple in character, as is the second. However, both take more time to determine than the very quick PQ method. The second of these additional measures is AQ (which symbolizes "Minimum Alley Quotient"). All three measures are compared in Table II. In the same manner as with PQ, the formulae for TQ and AQ were derived on the basis of the average values for man.

P is defined as the sum of all trials needed in learning the four-goal criteria. T is the same value with the exception that it excludes all the correct trials, even those not numbered among the 10 successful arrivals at each goal. P, on the other hand, includes even perfect trials when they are followed by error trials, which enter in to break the perfect learning series. Thus, T signifies the *minimum* number of error trials in the sense of the word just explained. The average T-value for man is 9.2 trials, and the average Trial Quotient for man (as with PQ) is arbitrarily placed at 100.

In the case of the Alley Quotient or AQ, A takes into account alley entrance errors rather than trial errors. A is defined as the sum total of all wrong alleys during the course of the running of the maze. This value ("minimum error-alleys") includes, also, those correct alleys in which, however, the animal subject only entered part way, and therefore did not reach the goal or find the food. The mean A-value for man was found to be 25.1 alleys. The average AQ for hominids, for the sake of consistency, was likewise set

---

* Time per trial could not be employed as a method of comparison (although it was always recorded and controlled by each animal's time limit), since animals of different orders of locomotory ability and speed were tested. In customary learning experiments, where only one species such as the rat is used, animals can be ranked on the basis of the three criteria, trials, errors (*i.e.* blind alley entrances, and the like, depending upon the type of learning apparatus employed), and time per trial. Table III in Ingebritsen's 1932[19] paper on the effect, on maze learning in rats, of operation on the cervical cord is a fine example of the combined use of all three of these criteria.

Table II

P, T, A Values and PQ, TQ, AQ Scores for Animals Tested in the Arrow Maze

Av'ge Rank Order	Animal	P	T	A	PQ	TQ	AQ	Av.Q
	Mammals and Birds (except EPT*):							
1	Man	14.8	9.2	25.1	100	100	100	100
2	Pig	31.8	21.8	46.7	46.5	42.2	53.7	47.5
3	Dog	38.4	26.1	40.4	38.5	35.2	62.1	45.3
	(EPT*	47	31.5	56.5	31.5	29.2	44.4	35)
	(Goat	54	37	56	27.4	24.9	44.8	32.4)
4.5	Chick	46.4	34.2	68.1	31.9	26.9	36.9	31.9
4.5	Rat	53.7	32.8	62.4	27.6	28	40.2	31.9
	(Rabbit	67	37	67	22.1	24.9	37.5	28.2)
6	Cat	61.1	43.1	89.5	24.2	21.3	28	24.5
	Reptiles							
	(Map T.	72	48	86	20.6	19.2	29.2	23)
7	Troost	113.6	82.4	129.5	13	11.2	19.4	14.5
8	Pond T.	119.3	78.3	166.3	12.4	11.7	15.1	13.1
9	Des. T.	128.3	82.3	153.4	11.5	11.2	16.4	13
10	Box T.	120	86.4	180	12.3	10.6	13.9	12.3

---

* Eastern Painted Turtle (only two specimens tested in maze). Only one subject was employed in the case of each of the other animals set off in parentheses.

at 100. The simplified formulae, derived in the same manner as the one for PQ, appear as follows:

$$TQ = 920/T$$
$$AQ = 2510/A$$

The rank order of animals, according to each of the three measures, PQ, TQ, and AQ, is to be found in Table III. Since all three measures are interrelated, each proves equally reliable and more or less interchangeable. The rank order coefficient of correlation† obtained for the three lists indicates a close similarity between the three different

---

† Spearman's formula, $\rho = 1 - \dfrac{6\Sigma(D^2)}{N(N^2-1)}$

scoring methods. The rank order, according to the PQ scores, had a .95 correlation with that of the values for TQ, and the same high correlation was obtained for TQ and AQ. .94.
Essentially the same, PQ correlated with AQ with a value of

Table III

Rank Order of Animals According to Three Learning Criteria

Rank	PQ	TQ	AQ	Average Q
1	Man	Man	Man	Man
2	Pig	Pig	Dog	Pig
3	Dog	Dog	Pig	Dog
4	Chick	Rat	Rat	⌠Rat
5	Rat	Chick	Chick	⌡Chick
6	Cat	Cat	Cat	Cat
7	Troost T.	Pond T.	Troost T.	Troost T.
8	Pond T.	⌠Troost T.	Desert T.	Pond T.
9	Box T.	⌡Desert T.	Pond T.	Desert T.
10	Desert T.	Box T.	Box T.	Box T.

Note: Equivalent ranks are indicated by a brace.

According to the values recorded in Table II, we note that the pig ranked second to man on all but the AQ score (53.7). Although the pig had fewer trials than the dog, it had more alley invasions. The dog, with fewer alley-errors, rated a higher AQ (62.1). Aside from this consideration, the dog rated third in average PQ, TQ, and average Q-score.

The chick and rat occupied fourth place, receiving almost identical scores. The chick had a little higher PQ (31.9 compared with 27.6 for the rat). However, their average Q was exactly the same (31.9). The rat had a poorer PQ because, more than in the case of the chick, it tended to spoil, by error, successful series of trials just before their completion.

Sixth in rank order, according to all three measures, came the common house cat.

At the bottom of our list (in seventh, eighth, ninth, and

tenth place) appear the four species of turtles, of which five or more specimens of each were tested in the maze.*

As will be seen from the column of P-values in Table II, the majority of the turtle species needed more than 100 trials in order to complete the four-alley maze routine. Add to this number the 40 correct trials necessary to complete the learning criteria, and it will be understood why the chelonians took so long to test. Furthermore, each individual trial was fairly long due to the generous time limit which the reptile group required. The alley invasions of this class of animals in our study also added up to a good deal over 100 on the average and sometimes, as in the Box Tortoise, almost reached 200. This value was more than twice that of the lowest animal in the rank order list of birds and mammals, the cat, which had an A-value of 89.5 alleys entered.

The average Q-scores placed the Troost Turtle first among the turtles, the Pacific Pond Turtle second, the Desert Tortoise third, and the Box Tortoise fourth and last. In the total series, all values except the TQ score were consistently at the level of seventh place in the Troost Turtle. In the case of the Western Pond Turtle, the average score placed it in eighth place, although TQ and AQ were slightly out of line. PQ and AQ are divergent in the case of the Desert Tortoise, but the average Q (13.0) places this form almost on a par with the Pond Turtle. The Box Tortoise, which ranked in tenth place, had an average Q-score of 12.3.

The two specimens of the Eastern Painted Turtle and

---

* With the exception of the Pacific Pond Turtle of the Western United States (*Clemmys marmorata*), some of which were too timid to be used in the maze. Only four animals proved tame enough to be manageable and usable, one of which was a baby *Clemmys* afraid of no object or living thing, and two more mature specimens from a river in Oregon, which had been in the laboratory for a whole year before being tested in the Arrow Maze. The latter animals were inured to handling and to the presence of the experimenter, and therefore they were reasonably tame. Even so, it is apparently the nature of water turtles to shy away from handling, more so than the land forms. The water turtle, apparently, feels less secure on the land, away from its normal element, while the land forms are habituated to depend upon their hard shell for security from outside attack.

the single Map Turtle presented startling scores. Both species rated a far higher average Q than any of the above four species of turtles. (These two reptile species are included in Table II, set off in parentheses, because of the insufficient number of individuals of each species tested.) The two Painted Turtles with an average Q-score of 35.0 ranked higher than the rat, chick, and cat, which had Q-scores of 31.9, 31.9, and 24.5, respectively. The two turtle species under discussion also attained a score that was from two to three times that of all the other four chelonian species. The single Map Turtle with an average Q of 23.0 was far above the remaining turtles.

The one goat that we tested fell a good deal below the dog, and almost on a level with both the chick and the rat. The single rabbit showed a score that placed it below the animals just mentioned, but distinctly above that of the cat. This, in spite of the greater difficulty in testing the rabbit, would indicate that this animal performed in the maze in a manner somewhat similar to the rat and possibly other rodents, with the exception of the slow-learning guinea pig. [8,12]

Table III omits the numerical values of the preceding table, and shows instead the rank order of the animal series according to each method of measurement, treated separately. This table is added for the sake of clarity.

The quantitative results with the 50 human subjects are interesting and worthy of comment at this point. The range of scores in the case of the hominid subjects was extremely wide, while the range in the infrahuman animals was more limited. Apparently, as one descends the biological scale, individual differences are less marked. For example, the range in the 50 human subjects was from a PQ of 50 to one of 336,* while in the 10 cats, it was 18 to 34, and in the 5 Box Tortoises, only 10 to 19. In the Desert Tortoise, on the other hand, where there were many more subjects than in the other chelonian species, the 27 individuals showed a

---

* These figures, for convenience, have been reduced to whole numbers.

range of 5 to 33 in Performance Quotient scores. This is a larger range than in those turtle species with fewer subjects.

But this relative difference in degree or range of individual performance may be only an artifact, since there were a great many more human subjects than individuals in each of the other species tested. In any event, with 50 subjects in the case of man, as compared with 10 or fewer for the majority of other animals in this study, it is to be expected that the hominid group might very easily present a wider range of scores.

After each individual of the hominid group had completed the maze problem, he was specifically asked in what way or ways he succeeded in learning the maze routine. The modes commonly employed in human maze learning, where vision is ruled out, were used here, namely, *verbal learning, visual imagery*, and *motor (or kinesthetic) clues.*

In verbal learning, the subject's subvocal speech rehearsed, so to speak, each turn to the right or left, each forward-going step or retracing behavior that he employed in reaching the goal in each trial. As he traced the maze pathways with his forefinger, he listed to himself each change of direction as he made it. This "verbal system" tended to become memorized in order to facilitate later learning, and to decrease the number of errors (wrong alleys entered), and the time consumed in each trial.

If the subject claimed to have employed visual learning, it was understood that, following the exploratory trials, he had developed a perceptual image of the maze pattern, based upon the tactile sensations of the exploring finger. But if there was no verbal system used, nor any clear visual imagery that would be helpful in learning the goal location, and if the subject seemed to rely upon the movement of the finger almost entirely, then the learning was considered motor or kinesthetic, and labeled as such.

In this assumed kinesthetic learning, the subject claims that he is "just feeling his way along through the maze," so to speak, and that his "mind is empty." Apparently, thought processes are essentially absent, and therefore cannot help in the learning process. These modes or categories are not too readily differentiated. But time was spent with each person after the trials had been completed, in order to define and discuss the three learning techniques, until the experimenter was convinced that the subject had a reasonably clear conception of their relative significance in his own learning. The subject was questioned in regard to the importance of each of these methods in his personal experience during the performance in the wire maze. On the basis of the introspective and analytic report of the subject, each of the three categories was given a weighted score according to the following simple system:

The most important factor, according to the introspective account of each subject, was assigned a value of 3, the next most important a score of 2, and the least important a score of 1. However, if only two factors were believed to have been involved, and one of these had very little apparent significance in the analysis of the subject's learning performance, then this latter factor was awarded a score of 1 only, rather than 2. If the two factors were both equally important in the subject's estimation, then each received the same score of 2. Those factors, apparently not involved at all, of course, were given a zero score. The assigned values were added up separately for the men and women, and then the final total score was obtained. These results are presented in Table IV. Percentage values (in parentheses) follow the numerical results.

Table IV

Methods Employed by the 50 Human Subjects in Learning the Finger Maze Replica of the Arrow Maze

Subjects	Verbal	Visual	Motor	Total
Women	6 (5.5%)	64 (50.7%)	56 (43.8%)	126 (100%)
Men	4 (4.8%)	37 (50.8%)	32 (44.4%)	73 "
Men & Women	10 (5 %)	101 (50.8%)	88 (44.2%)	199 "
Summary	5%	51%	44%	100%

It is apparent from the values in Table IV that visual imagery was the most important factor in learning the Arrow Maze for these 50 human subjects. Visual imagery was employed approximately 50% of the time, but motor learning or kinesthetic imagery followed as a close second in about 45% of the cases. Verbal processes, on the other hand, appeared in only 5% of the subjects. The dominant importance of motor and visual learning in finger mazes is fairly consistent with previous work, as for example that of Husband in 1931.[20]

However, with stylus mazes, where the finger does not contact the maze surface, verbal formulae may prove more important in learning than the other two factors, as was found by Warden.[21] (Kinesthetic cues in the latter type of hominid maze are of course decreased to a great extent by the use of an implement to replace the forefinger in gliding through the alley grooves.)

From the above table it is apparent that there was no significant difference in the relative importance of the various methods used in running the maze by the two sexes. In fact, the results for the men and women were extraordinarily alike! However, there was a sex difference in PQ scores which, although not marked, was still large considering the number of subjects averaged. The average PQ for the 32 women was 97 (in round numbers), while the 18 men averaged 8 points higher, or 105. Possibly the men were motivated to a slightly higher degree, but this was not at all our impression. Both sexes seemed to express a similarly keen interest in doing their best in the problem situation, and they were always eager to know how their performance compared with that of other subjects. The competitive spirit maintained the degree of motivation at a high level.

Perhaps the men felt that they *had* to do well in relation to the women, and therefore approached the problem with more dogged purpose and serious intent. But it seems more logical, after weighing the behavioral responses and other considerations in regard to the subjects, that the difference in average scores probably was representative of a true difference in learning capacity or speed of performance in the two sexes.

The range of scores for the men was from 55 to 280 PQ, and for the women from 50 to 336, the highest PQ score being thus attained by a woman. From these results, it would seem to be the case that the men were more consistent and tended to cluster around the mean to a greater degree in their scores, while the women were more variable. However, there were more women than men (almost twice as many, 32 as opposed to 18). For this reason alone, we might suspect the range of scores for the women to be wider.

We could not consider sex differences in all of the animals tested. Due to the conflicting influence of the estrus cycle in the ♀ rat, all of the experimental rats which we tested in the Arrow Maze were ♂ ♂. As for the chelonians, this group has also been omitted from mention in this regard, because of the uncertainty of sex differentiation, especially in very young specimens.

In man, as stated above, the ♂ ♂ were slightly superior in learning performance score. The same was found in the case of the pig and cat, although the difference in the latter was hardly significant. In the dog, different breeds were employed, and as a group the ♀ ♀ performed better than the ♂ ♂. Whether this would occur if all the dogs had been of the same breed is doubtful, but at present not known. In the case of the 10 chicks, the two sexes ranked almost exactly the same.

The above results, concerning sex differences in learning performance, are summarized specifically in Table V. This table indicates that the average for all of the animal forms listed places the ♂ ♂ at a slight advantage over the ♀ ♀ in learning speed. But this difference is so small in our study as to be considered almost negligible.

Table V

Sex Differences in Learning Performance:
Average PQ Score for Each Sex in Man, Pig, Dog, Chick, and Cat

Animal	Sex	No. of S's	Average P-Value	Average PQ(1480/P)
Man	♀	32	15.2	97.4 (97)
	♂	18	14.1	105 (105)
Pig	♀	5	37.2	39.8 (40)
	♂	4	25	59.2 (59)
Dog	♀	4	34	43.5 (44)
	♂	6	41.3	35.8 (36)
Chick	♀	6	46	32.2 (32)
	♂	4	47	31.5 (32)
Cat	♀	5	63	23.5 (24)
	♂	5	59.2	25 (25)

Combined Results, ♀ ♀ *vs.* ♂ ♂

Average P-Values

Sex	Man	Pig	Dog	Chick	Cat	Total	Av. P	Av. PQ
♀	15.2	37.2	34	46	63	195.4	39.1	37.9(38)
♂	14.1	25	41.3	47	59.2	186.6	37.3	39.7(40)

The reader may be interested in comparing the present results, as obtained by the use of the Arrow Maze, with the vast amount of maze work on animals that has been done in the last quarter of a century, especially on the white rat. If we consider the results for only the first goal in the Arrow Maze, *i.e.* to alley #3 alone, we have a maze situation more nearly similar to the method employed in preceding experiments. When a rat, for example, is tested in a Multiple-T Maze, there is normally but one goal (the food compartment at the end of the complex pathway) to be learned.

Table VI compares the rank order of learning ability with one goal (alley #3) and with the regular four-goal routine of the Arrow Maze. Learning the first goal in the Arrow Maze is similar to learning a single goal in the Multiple-T Maze. It will be seen from Table VI that the two lists are very similar, and in fact have a very high correlation by Spearman's formula of .93.

Table VI

Rank Order* of Performance in Learning a Single Goal Compared With Learning Four Successive Goals in the Arrow Maze

Single-Goal Problem	Multi-Goal Problem
Man	Man
Dog	Pig
Pig	Dog
Chick	Chick
Cat	Rat
Rat	Cat
Chelonians†	Chelonians

---

* Correlation by Spearman's formula between the two rank orders is very high, .93.

† The four species listed in Table III: Troost Turtle, Pacific Pond Turtle, Desert Tortoise, and Box Tortoise.

From Table VI we may conclude that in immediate learning the dog is superior to the less stable pig, and similarly the cat is superior to the rat. However, in the "long pull," the evidence would seem to imply that the pig and the rat pick up learning speed and develop a habit routine with greater facility than the dog and the cat, respectively.

We shall now consider the average results for the four goals of the Arrow Maze, each taken separately. Table VII lists the average P-values for each alley, expressed in terms of percentage of the total P-value for each animal form. These percentages are finally averaged to indicate the proportion of time spent in learning each alley. From this table we may draw the following conclusions: Alley #2 may take more or less time to learn than #3, depending on whether practice in learning the first alley is a help or a handicap in learning the second. If alley #3 interferes with the learning of alley #2, then the previous practice in the first alley is a stumbling block rather than an aid to the subject. The averages for the first two goals are almost the same. Man, rat, and the four species of chelonians improved on the second alley, and therefore seemed to profit by previous experience in running the maze. Confusion between the two alleys was apparently strong in the pig, dog, chick, and cat, whose average number of trials increased in the learning of the second goal.

Table VII

Per Cent of Trials to Each Goal in the Arrow Maze

Animal	Goal: Alley No.:	I 3	II 2	III 4	IV 1	Total %
Man		31.1%	24.3%	27.7%	16.9%	(100%)
Pig		24.8	27.4	27.7	20.1	"
Dog		18.2	28.6	40.6	12.5	(99.9)
Chick		17.7	23.3	29.1	30.0	(100.1)
Rat		31.2	20.6	23.6	24.5	(99.9)
Cat		18.5	27.8	29.5	24.2	(100)
Chelonians		35.8	13.2	23.4	27.6	"
Average		25.3	23.6	28.8	22.3	"

The next generality that we may consider is that alley #4 practically always necessitates more trials for learning than alley #2, probably because of more interference with the learning of the previous goals, #3 and #2.

Alley #1, the final goal site, normally takes less learning time than is required for alley #4; occasionally, it takes more time, if the learning of the previous goals proves more of a hindrance than the preceding practice proves an advantage.

Thus we see that alleys #3 and #2 take about the same number of trials to learn, depending upon the animal tested. Alley #4 takes longer than #2 or #1, while alley #1, the final goal, generally rates the least number of errors. The reason for this is that the animal has usually become accustomed to the maze routine, and the interference of other goals is not as distracting as at first.

Another reason why alley #1 is learned in the shortest time of all may be the result of "experimental extinction" which erases, so to speak, the former goals as possible locations of the food. (The presentation of this theory is offered in another section of this work.)

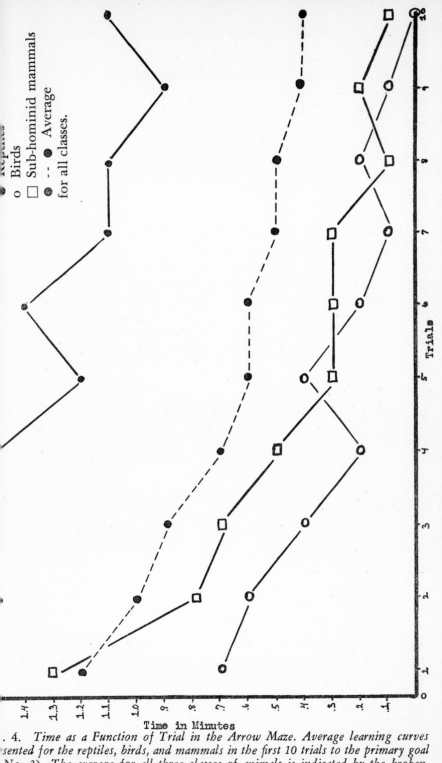

Fig. 4. *Time as a Function of Trial in the Arrow Maze. Average learning curves presented for the reptiles, birds, and mammals in the first 10 trials to the primary goal No. 3). The average for all three classes of animals is indicated by the broken- ve. (The values on which the reptile curve was based were reduced to 1/10 in o accommodate them to the size of the graph.)*

Because of the great variations in the number of trials required to learn each goal, it was impractical to construct comparative learning curves for the entire set of trials for all animals, even when only one of the goals was considered. (A turtle might require 100 trials to complete the learning of the first goal, while a dog might take only a half dozen trials before beginning the successful run of criterion trials.) Instead, the average time for each of the first 10 trials in the learning of the primary goal (alley #3) was computed for each animal form.

In Fig. 4, a graph is presented, showing the learning curves for these 10 initial trials of the following classes of animals: the reptiles (the four species of chelonians listed in Table III), the birds (the Hampshire Red chickens), and the mammals (the pig, dog, rat, and cat).

Man is omitted from the mammalian average, because of the fact that his learning speed was so rapid that only one error-trial might occur prior to the 10 successive correct trials to the primary goal. Also, the time consumed in a Finger Maze, such as the one employed with the human subjects, is not equivalent to the time spent in the floor maze.

The curves, as can be seen from the graph, are reasonably smooth when one considers the small number of subjects representing each class. Furthermore, on the basis of research by others in the past, the normal fluctuation from trial to trial is expected in learning curves. If 100 or more subjects had been averaged for each class, the curves would probably have approached or even surpassed the regularity apparent in the curve averaging all three classes. This average curve for all the animals in our study is indicated by the dotted line on the graph.

The reason why the curves do not drop more steeply apparently is due to the fact that there is actually very little improvement—as might be expected—in these first few trials. If they are "J-curves," they are very flat ones, without a significantly large initial drop in the first few trials. However, there is evidence to be derived from the curves, and from the original data which formed the basis of these curves, that a fair amount of improvement occurred from the very first.

The mammals, as a group, showed the greatest improvement in the first 10 trials, *i.e.* the decrease in time per trial was the most marked within this period. The chick, which showed less improvement between the first and tenth trials, did not improve at the same rate as the mammals. This may be due simply to the fact that it began at a higher level of speed, and there was therefore less room for improvement.

The curve for the birds is more erratic than that for the mammals, but the reason for this is probably the difference in the number of species which each curve represents. The mammalian curve represents four species, while the bird curve illustrates only one species. Considered broadly, the two curves are very similar and, in fact, contact and overlap each other at points in the latter half of the series of trials, graphically depicted in Fig. 4.

Even more erratic than the bird curve is the one representing the reptiles. But in this case, the lack of smoothness is more striking, and cannot be associated with the use of only a single species. In actuality, as with the mammalian curve, four species are averaged, in this instance two water turtle forms (the Troost Turtle and the Pacific Pond Turtle) and two land tortoises (the California Desert Tortoise and the New Jersey Box Tortoise).

On inspecting the individual chelonian records, it is easy to understand why the curve for this group of animals is not more uniform. There was much fluctuation in the time consumed in each trial, especially in the primary ones before habit patterns had been set down, and while exploratory and trial-and-error behavior was more clearly in evidence than in later trials. The turtles, in general, were so much slower in their learning performance that the figures for the turtle curve had to be reduced to one-tenth in order to accommodate them to the limits of the graph.

The fact that the chelonian curve indicates that these animals did not improve much in the first 10 trials, is simply an expression of the true state of affairs. At the completion of the tenth trial, the turtle, in comparison with the pig, is at a much lower level of completion of the goal criterion, since the pig learns so much more quickly. The first few trials of the turtle appeared essentially exploratory; on the other hand, at this stage the pig was already beginning the 10 successive correct trials to alley #3 that satisfy the criterion of learning for the primary goal. Some turtles, indeed, showed little real improvement in performance even at the end of 20 or 30 trials.

We were interested in discovering whether other tests of learning ability would yield results that correlated with those obtained by the use of the Arrow Maze. Accordingly, as an additional experiment, the behavior of 15 Desert Tortoises was studied in the maze, Trip Box, and Ring Box. (The two problem boxes have been described at length, under II. Method.)

These puzzle boxes were of different degrees of difficulty. The door of the Trip Box opened when the animal stepped or pressed upon the wire near the entrance. It was less complicated and less demanding of manipulatory ability than the Ring Box. The latter puzzle box required more exact skill, and could rarely be opened by chance movements of the tortoise.

Rank order correlations were extremely low. The order of 15 tortoise subjects in the maze and Trip Box produced a correlation of only .38 (Spearman's formula), and the maze and Ring Box a correlation of .21. Surprisingly enough, the lowest correlation was discovered between the two problem boxes themselves, only .06. We expected that the correlation of the two puzzle boxes would be better than that of either one with the maze situation.

It should be mentioned here that all three learning problems were presented to the Desert Tortoise concurrently, because of the many months needed to complete each series of trials. Correlation of results between the performance scores of the individual turtles might have been better if the problems had been presented one at a time over a period of a few years. In any case, only 1 or 2 trials in each apparatus per day were imposed upon these particular subjects to prevent fatigue and loss of the high degree of motivation necessary for any success at all.

Nevertheless, there seemed to be a general leveling-off of performance during the trials on a particular day. For example, a turtle quickly proceeded through the first apparatus in which it was placed, because its level of motivation was initially at its peak. When it was ready for its trials in the third apparatus, motivation would still be strong because of the small number of trials already given. Nevertheless, it is obvious that the drive to seek food could not be as impelling as it was in the first apparatus. Because of this situation, the order of performance in the three learning problems was altered from day to day. If the maze came first for all subjects on one day, it followed second on the next day, while one of the problem boxes was employed first. This procedure prevented undue weighting of the results, and presumably tended to equalize or neutralize any disturbing factors that might have been present.

Perhaps interference between the different types of learning problems served to erase any indication of possible transfer of training that might have been present, especially between the two problem boxes. The boxes could both be opened to permit escape to the food by pressure applied in the appropriate place. Learning the mode of escape in one might have facilitated the learning of the second. Furthermore, one would expect that the tortoise which learned one escape box in a relatively small number of trials would likewise learn quickly in the second box. However, this only applied to a small number of the subjects. The wide disparity of the results for the majority of the animals tested in the two problem boxes accounts for the very low correlation between the two.

Placing the tortoises in three successive problem situations each day was possibly too strenuous a routine for these reptiles of low energy reserve. With a less demanding program, spread over a longer period of time, the resulting correlations might have been more demonstrative of some relation of individual ability in various learning situations. It is difficult to accept, without further study, the implication from these limited results that the learning of each separate problem was a function completely isolated from the other problems. A quick learner in one situation was not, necessarily, a fast learner in all similar problems.

In connection with the above discussion, for a moment we might return to the question of suitability of a maze in comparative work. The author is convinced that the maze situation, as a learning tool, is a superior measure of relative learning ability in animals. The reason for this is that no extraordinary skills of a manipulatory sort are required, the animal needing only the necessary means of locomotion in order to reach the goal where the food is concealed. This uncomplicated arrangement permits the lower classes of vertebrates to perform without the handicap arising from the possession of inferior skills, as compared with the superior abilities of higher classes of animals.

Over the long period of time covered by the experiments, it was noted that during a certain trial the behavior of the subjects was superior to what would be expected on the basis of mere chance. The particular trial which we have in mind was the primary one in the learning of the final goal site, namely, alley #1.

This critical trial followed the change of maze incentive from alley #4 to #1. The animal had just completed the 10 successive trials that fulfilled the criterion of learning for alley #4. On the eleventh trial, it was interesting to see what it would do if no reward was present. After entering alley #4 once more, and no longer finding food there, he retraced his steps and then had a 50:25:25 chance of entering alleys #3, #2, and #1, respectively.*

There was, first, a 50:50 chance of his entering alley #3, or else continuing further down the neutral zone of the maze

---

* Expectancy on the basis of "statistical chance" (exclusive of other factors); i.e. two behavioral possibilities at each of two successive choice points.

(*i.e.* the area in front of, but not including, the four alleys). Proceeding further in the same direction, and also on the basis of pure chance, there was then a 50:50 possibility of his entry into either of the two remaining alleys, #2 or #1. Since only 50% of the total possible decisions of the animal are left, this number must be divided equally between these latter two pathways. Thus we have the 50:25:25 chance ratio.

If one selected a sufficiently large number of subjects, one would actually get these figures, *provided there were no interfering factors that would distort the normal expected results.* Nevertheless, with only 40 control animals, we obtained a fairly close approximation of the above ratios. These 40 control subjects had not been previously employed in the maze and were ignorant of its pattern.

There were 10 hominid subjects. 10 dogs, 10 cats, and 10 albino rats. The Finger Maze (see the pattern of this copy of the larger floor maze in the first figure of the Appendix) was employed in the case of the human subjects, while the regular large maze was used with the animal subjects. The human subjects were allowed to wander through the maze pathways entirely at random, and the path which they took each time after leaving alley #4 was recorded. Fifty such records were taken for each subject.

For the animals, it was found convenient and quicker to employ alley #4 as the starting point in each of a series of 50 trials per subject, recording in each case the first alley entered after leaving alley #4. (The inner section of alley #4 was blocked off to prevent loss of time in wandering therein, and thus to accelerate the progress of the trials.) Since these were control trials to determine free choice of alley entry by each subject, without the presence of influential factors, no food was present anywhere in the maze.

The chance results, obtained in the above manner, for the 40 animals were as follows. Alley #3 was entered 56% of the time (not far from the 50% figure, predicted on the basis of chance); alley #2 was invaded 24% of the trials; and alley #1 was entered 21% of the time.

Among the hominid subjects, the 5 ♀ ♀ averaged 25.2% entries into alley #1, while the 5 ♂ ♂ entered this alley in about the same frequency, or 26.8% of the time. The average for both sexes was 26%.

The 4 ♀ dogs and 6 ♂ ♂ averaged exactly the same in frequency of entry into the pathway in question. Alley #1 was entered 22% of the time by each sex, and the average for both sexes, of course, was this same figure.

The 6 ♀ cats entered alley #1 15% of their trials, the 4 ♂ ♂ 15.5%, and the average for both sexes was 15.2%. It is not understood why the per cent for these kittens was below the 25% expected value, but possibly a forward-going tendency into the first alleys encountered after leaving alley #4 might have been strong in these subjects.

In the case of the rat subjects, only 1 young ♂ was available at the time, which accounts for the fact that the remaining 9 specimens chosen were ♀ ♀. These ♀ ♀ gave a 20.7% average entry into the critical alley, while the single ♂ entered this pathway 28% of the time. The average for the 10 animals was 21.4%.

Table VIII gives a rank-order picture of the various animals in our study in regard to the correctness of the "critical trial" discussed above. By correct response in this trial we simply mean that the animal went directly from alley #4 to the new goal, alley #1, on the very first trial involving the latter pathway. In order to do this, the animal had to pass the entrances to both alley #3 and #2, which were the nearer pathways and the first ones the animal confronted after leaving #4.

It will be noted from the table that 7 out of 10, or 70% of the species, had scores in this test above 25% or pure chance.* The actual rank order, however, is inconsistent with the phyletic order. This may be due to actual differences in ability or physiological makeup, or merely to variations in the number of subjects per animal form tested. Man

---

* However, a lack of statistical significance was indicated by the critical ratios between these values and the predicted percentages (see Table VIII).

Table VIII

Rank Order of Ten Species According to Performance Level
in the Critical Primary Trial to the Fourth Goal
in the Arrow Maze

Species	No. of S's	% of Correct Trials	Critical Ratio*
Desert T.	27	50	2.0
Man	50	41	1.7
Cat	10	40	0.7
Pig	9	33	0.4
Rat	20	33	0.6
Troost T.	6	33	0.3
Pac. Pond T.	4	33	0.3
Box T.	5	20	0.2
Dog	10	20	0.3
Chick	10	0	1.8

* This is an index of the reliability of a difference between two measures, in this case the actual per cents obtained and the percentages calculated solely on the basis of "pure chance." A critical ratio of 3 or more indicates that the obtained difference is statistically significant, *i.e.* the chances are greater than 999 in 1000 that a true difference exists.

and the Desert Tortoise, which head the list, had the highest number of subjects in the present study, namely, 50 and 27 subjects, respectively.

Each animal had learned to go to three of the alleys in the Arrow Maze, in order to locate the food incentive in each successive goal. Thus there was merely one goal site remaining, and that was, of course, alley #1. The fact that some of the animals passed *directly* from #4 to the new alley, #1, in the very first trial might lead one to suppose, at first glance, that "insight" was involved. But the temptation to label such behavior by this term should be avoided. Morgan's canon, or the law of parsimony, serves to prevent our assuming something that may not be true in this particular case.

We believe that the subjects, in general, did not consciously realize that the one pathway left to serve as the goal was alley #1. A more mechanistic explanation is preferable. Such a one is the concept employed by Pavlov and later research workers with the conditioned reflex technique, namely, that of "experimental extinction."

Extinction can and probably does explain the results in an adequate and satisfactory manner. From the standpoint of this concept, we shall analyze the animal subject's behavior in the Arrow Maze. After the animal had completed the learning of the first goal, alley #3, the food was no longer placed in this region, but only in pathway #2. Each time the animal then entered #3 and found nothing there, the chances were lessened that it would again enter the unsatisfactory pathway. In other words, the subject was thus forced to pass through a period in which the habitual response to alley #3 was progressively deconditioned or extinguished, until a stage was reached in which the pathway tended to be avoided rather than approached and entered.

The actual individual records for the various animals would seem to corroborate this extinction theory. There are fewer and fewer entries into alley #3, while at the same time the exploration of the remaining alleys is increased.

Entries into alley #3 gradually diminish and finally disappear, at which time the 10 correct trials to the second goal occur. As an example, in the case of M-4, one of the Desert Tortoises, the trials immediately following the completion of the learning of the primary goal were as follows: 3-4-3-4-2, 3-2, 3-2, 3-4-2, 2, 3-2, 3-2, 3-2, 2, 2, 3-2, a row of eight trials to 2, 3-4-4-4-2, followed by the 10 successive criterion trials to alley #2.

In Levinian (or topological) terminology, we might say that alley #3 now has a neutral valence (not minus, since there is no punishment for entering this alley), while alley #2, the next goal, now bears a plus valence. The remaining alleys are also neutral until their turn comes for service as the goal. The conditioned habit of entering alley #3 is replaced by one of entering the second alley. By the time the new goal is learned, alley #3 is avoided in almost every trial, but may be entered again for a few times after the incentive is changed to alley #4. Extinction will work in the same way in the case of alley #2, while the learning of #4 is being perfected.

We return now to consider the critical trial discussed above. The animal leaves alley #4, because food is no longer there. Due to the effect of the previous experimental extinction on alleys #3 and #2, the subject may skip both of these and enter alley #1 directly. Alley #1 is the only possibility that remains. On the other hand, many subjects approach the problem of finding the new goal site in a manner which one would have to consider logical. This technique of response to the new situation is an entry into each alley in turn (#3-#2-#1) until the food is located. Many subjects, especially the slower turtle group, perform in just this way, after leaving the empty goal in alley #4. However, the highest percentage in Table VIII (p. 73) was attained by a member of this group, the Desert Tortoise. This species showed a result twice that of chance, or 50% correct first trials to alley #1. The scores of the remaining members of the reptile group were lower.

The present study, in regard to the reptile class, indicates beyond a doubt that chelonians, although slow in locomotion, are nevertheless capable of displaying a fairly high degree of learning ability and retention, comparable to many of the higher vertebrates. This would be true, of course, only in the type of problem situation not involving manipulatory motor skills, which the turtles are morphologically and neurally incapable of developing. Learning the maze, admittedly, took many trials for this class, but all four goals were successively and successfully attained. No species, in fact, was found that could not complete the performance problem presented to it in the Arrow Maze. This, despite the fact that some of the turtles demanded an excessive degree of patience in testing on the part of the experimenter.

But more impressive than the learning ability of the reptiles was their capacity for retention of previous learning performance. Special additional experiments indicated that the dog forgot the last-learned goal in less than a month's time, while the turtle remembered to go to alley #1 for food, after an interval of over a month and a half. Retention might be of longer duration in these reptiles (and probably is, from a consideration of Casteel's [2] research on the Central

Painted Turtle, a fresh-water species which showed evidence of retention with very few errors after as long as 3 to 4 months. In this case, the learning problem was one of visual discrimination between black lines of different widths). However, in the case of the chelonians, no interval tests of a longer duration than 50 days were conducted. With increasing intervals from 1 to 50 days, there was only a very *gradual* decrease in performance skill and a slow increase in errors and time per trial.

At the 50-day interval, some turtles still went straight to path #1, without first entering any of the other alleys. This was contrary to the general inclination in most animals to pursue a forward-going tendency (discussed elsewhere in this work), which would have led the turtles either into alley #3 or alley #2, before finding their way to the food in #1.

Retention tests on the Desert Tortoises were made not only in the case of the Arrow Maze, but also with the two problem boxes. When the intervals between the trials were increased up to 50 days, the average time per trial in the Trip and Ring Boxes doubled or tripled. This was by no means a small increase, but in no case did this time level approach to any degree the time limit for turtles, or the average time in the primary trials when the problem was first being learned. In other words, the learning curve was not symmetrical at both ends, and would not be so until larger intervals of time were employed between individual trials. Surprisingly enough, in the puzzle boxes and also in the maze, there was a sudden increase in average time per trial of 100% between the final daily trials and the one-day interval trials, where a day without testing intervened between two testing days. Apparently, the lapse of a single day without experimental trials was a serious interruption of the normal practice routine and a handicap for the chelonians.

A lapse of a single day would, we believe, make little difference in the case of mammals or birds. On the other hand, the difference between these primary "interval trials" and the final 50-day interval test was negligible! The initial increase in time required for each trial was maintained with fluctuations during the interval trials, but did not generally get any worse.

The chelonian species, *Clemmys marmorata* and *Pseudemys scripta troostii,* the Pacific Pond Turtle and the Troost Turtle, respectively, both displayed similar figures in regard to retention. A 100% increase in time per trial occurred between no interval and one-day interval trials. The maximum interval tests closed with figures that were two to three times the temporal values for the first interval trial.

The above discussion may seem to imply that the reptile has better retention than the mammal or bird. But there is one contributing causal factor that we must not overlook. The pig learned the entire maze routine within one week, while the turtle needed as long as six months to complete successfully the learning of the four different goals. This means that the reptile had the advantage of many times more practice trials in the case of the final goal (alley #1) than did the pig, or any of the other higher vertebrates tested.

The case is clear: Because the habit of learning to go to the final goal in pathway #1 for the food took so long to develop in the turtle, compared with the pig. for example, it is not at all surprising that this habit persisted for a longer time, and that therefore the evidence of retention or revival of the old habit would be stronger in the case of the reptile. When an interval of more than a month intervened before further testing, the turtle still gave evidence of preserving the former well-developed habit of heading straight for the final goal, since this performance pattern took so long to organize. The pig or the dog, on the other hand, learned so rapidly that the retention of the learning of *all four* goals might be almost of the same order of magnitude, and confusion would therefore result.

The dog, for example, in later interval trials would perhaps still recall obtaining food in, let us say, alley #4 (the next to the last goal) almost as clearly as in alley #1. (This seemed to be the actual case, as deduced from retention experiments on the dog.) The turtle, however, would have less chance of remembering food in #4, since this goal had been learned such a long time previously due to its slower rate of performance speed.

Thus, in our study, we may conclude that the turtle exhibits such relatively good and persistent retention (in comparison with that of the higher vertebrates) only because its last-developed habit pattern has had such a long period to become ingrained within the psychobiological mechanisms of the animal. A man's vivid imagery of an occurrence that happened to him at the age of four has probably no analogue in the neural experience of a turtle.

After the data for the present research had been collected, it was considered desirable to make a more minute statistical analysis of the learning function of an animal in the Arrow Maze. For this special treatment of the data, the Desert Tortoise was the species selected. It was chosen for two reasons. First, the chelonians as a group required the greatest number of trials to learn each goal location, and therefore afforded the largest amount of learning data with which to deal.

Secondly, the Desert Tortoise was the chelonian species in our experimental list in which the greatest number of subjects (27) was employed. This meant the most available data. The reason for our use of so many specimens of *Gopherus agassizii* was, as previously stated, our special interest in the reptile class.

The first problem that challenged us concerned the question of combining the separate data for each of the four goals, in order to gain a clear comprehensive picture of the Arrow Maze learning situation as a whole. All four learning situations were treated in a uniform manner, and interrelated by analyzing them in terms of the following categories: the pathway which contains the goal site, the nearest alley to the goal path, the next nearest alley, and the most distant path from the goal in each case. The four learning situations were combined in this manner as summarized in Table IX.

Table IX

Technique for Combining the Separate Data for Each of the Four Goals in the Arrow Maze

Learning Situation	Goal Location	Nearest Alley to Goal	Next Nearest Alley	Distant Alley
I	Alley #3	2	4	1
II	Alley #2	3	1	4
III	Alley #4	3	2	1
IV	Alley #1	2	3	4

In every case, as will be seen from the table, the nearest alley to the goal was defined as the one not only next to the goal alley, but also nearest to the maze entrance. Most animals, apparently, have a normal forward-going tendency (as it has been termed in the literature on the subject) which in this maze caused alleys #3 and #2 to be entered more often than the more distant and lateral alleys (#1 and #4).

By the above arrangement, the results for the four alleys in the case of the 27 *Gopherus* tortoises were combined and averaged. When only the first alley entered in each trial was considered, it was found that the goal alley was entered 58% of the time, the nearest alley to the goal 24% of the trials, the next nearest 12%, and the far alley only 6%. These findings revealed the logical effect of the influence of the proximity of the goal site. When the total alleys per trial were added, we found that the goal alley received a higher percentage of entries at the expense of the other three alleys which had a lower per cent. The goal attracted 68% of all approaches, the nearest alley in each case an average of 18%, the next nearest path 9%, and the far alley in this case only 5%.

It is apparent, as brought out also by the actual recorded observations in the case of each animal in the maze, that when errors did occur, it was more likely that they would take place in the immediate vicinity of the correct alley, at a time when it had not as yet been clearly distinguished from the other pathways.

The next project was to discover if there was indeed a real forward-going tendency in the tortoise during the learning process. In other words, would a tortoise enter an alley directly in front of it in preference to alleys on either side, or at a distance from it? This was tested. All four learning situations were averaged, this time in their normal order of alley #1, #2, #3, and #4. Under this condition, the results for the four goals should normally give an equal number of invasions of each pathway. The weighting in favor of alley #3, when this was the goal site, would be neutralized by the weighting of alley #2 when the latter was favored as the goal, and so on for each new goal location. We would expect 25% of alley entries to be accorded to each pathway.

On the contrary, the results on tabulating the first alley entered in each trial gave alleys #2 and #3 the highest percentages, 35% each, while alley #1 received only about 10% of the animal entries, and alley #4 twice this amount. Percentages were then determined for "total alleys entered" per trial (rather than just the first pathway invaded in each trial, as above). These were 16%, 32%, 29%, and 23% for alleys #1 to #4, respectively.

From the above results, we see that the central alleys on the average were entered about twice as often as the lateral alleys. It would seem that a forward-going tendency was certainly operating, and that the turtle more naturally entered the alley openings directly in front of him (after passing through the archway in the front of the maze at the beginning of a trial) than those on either side, and at a distance from the entrance. What is more, we notice that alley #4 received a greater number of entries than alley #1.

Is there also a right-going tendency in this particular species? (It will be recalled that in experiments dealing with visual discrimination of animals, the subjects sometimes got into so-called "position habits" of selecting the path, say, to the right in every trial, even if punishment occurred as often as reward for such behavior, or the animal selected the stimulus presented on one side always because it happened to occur on that side, regardless of the nature of the stimulus itself.) To answer the question posed above, tests of directional preference were conducted with the entire group of 27 Desert Tortoises, and the results were averaged.

There was little or no indication in these results of a right-going tendency. There was a statistical difference in the preference for the two alleys, but this was so slight as to be of doubtful significance. Fifty-two per cent of unmotivated turns were to the right of the entrance of the Arrow Maze, while 48% of the turns were to the left.

The most logical explanation, therefore, of the above dominance of alley #4 over alley #1 would seem to involve behavioral habits set up in the learning of the very first goal. Since the primary goal was to the *right* of the entrance, *i.e.* to alley #3, there is the strong possibility that a physiological tendency of mild intensity developed in this direction, and was never entirely obliterated by learning the two alleys on the left side of the maze (#2 and #1).

It was stated in the beginning of II. Method that alley #3 was chosen as the primary goal, although alley #2 might have served as well, in order to keep the first problem in the maze from being too difficult and thus possibly causing the animal to lose interest at the very outset. It was also stated that the subject in the maze in the first trials would have the tendency to go straight ahead from the entrance and enter the nearest alley. Now, from the above experiments, we have statistical proof that this was a true assumption. The question of the goal's proximity to the beginning point of a maze is an important primary consideration in all learning problems employing such apparatus.

We have already briefly mentioned the influence of the length of the interval between trials on the maze-learning performance in certain of our species, namely the turtles. Because these animals had attracted the least amount of previous study, we were most interested in them. In these tests of the effect of time lapse, the last-learned goal, alley #1, remained the correct incentive location henceforth. The time intervals serially expanded from 1 day between successive groups of trials to a maximum of 50 days.

Averaging the results for these special trials gave further evidence of the normal distribution of alley entries in a four-parallel-pathway arrangement such as the Arrow Maze. Alley #1 was the goal and was, of course, on the extreme left side of the maze. The nearest alley to the correct one was alley #2, the next-nearest path was #3, and the most distant pathway from the location of the goal was alley #4.

The gradient here is interesting: For the results of the first alley entered in each trial, alley #4 was invaded only 10% of the interval trials; #3, 14%; #2, 16%; and #1, the goal, was entered 60% of the time.

Considering the total number of alleys entered in each trial (rather than just the first entry in each case), we obtained the following averages: alleys #4 to #1 were entered 7%, 9%, 11%, and 73% of the time, respectively. It was apparent from these expected results that the farther an alley was from the actual goal, the less chance was there that the tortoise would be induced to enter it. Mistaking alley #2 for #1 was more common than making the same error in the case of the remaining two alleys. In this case, the forward-going tendency was more or less subordinated to a left-going tendency, temporarily developed, with an increase in the chance of entering a pathway as the animal traveled farther toward the left.

It is logical to suppose that, good or poor as the retention of an animal might be, the chances of his entering a wrong alley were fewer in direct proportion to the distance of the alley from the correct one. This might be expressed in terms of a mathematical law, enabling prediction of animal behavior in such a restricted situation. This direct correlation of distance from the goal with amount of activity would be even more impressive in the case of a maze with a series of 10 alleys laid side by side. The fact that the differences between the first three percentages in the above figures were exactly the same (7%, 9%, 11% for alleys #4, #3, and #2, respectively, all giving a difference of 2% between each other) indicated that each alley further from the correct one had an *equal* additional decrease in chance of invasion by the animal subject.

V. DISCUSSION

THE PRESENT STUDY ESSENTIALLY CENTERS AROUND DATA collected by the use of animals tested in the Arrow Maze. Considered broadly, the results reveal the following facts regarding the relative level of learning performance or ability in the several animal forms employed. To the human subject was assigned the highest level of performance, namely, a PQ of 100. The pig's level was next at about half this figure or a PQ of about 50. The third level, a PQ in the neighborhood of 40, included the dog, while the chicken appeared at a level of 30. The rodents and the remaining mammals on our list were about 25, while the reptiles came at the bottom of the list with an average Performance Quotient of about 15. Thus the results take the form of a diminuendo, and the animals place themselves on the scale somewhat in accordance with their status on the biological scale.

It is most interesting that there is such a coincidence between rank order in learning ability in the Arrow Maze and phyletic order. The rank order of performance seems to follow the order of the biological scale. One is induced to inquire why this is so, and to consider, therefore, the physiological mechanisms of behavior that may be partly responsible.

These animals are anatomically and physiologically different. Some possess prehensile members constructed for a particular type of performance. The chicken's wings make possible flight over short distances, while its strong, powerful leg muscles permit grasping of a perch pole or other object. The dog, cat, and rat move their external members in almost prehensile fashion. But the pig and the goat can not, due to a different arrangement of musculature in the forelegs. The turtle, of course, lacks any real sort of prehensile type of physical equipment. It can only grasp an object effectively with the aid of its strong jaws. On the other hand, the rat (which does not require the support of at least three of its legs at one time, as in the case of the turtle, except when relaxed on the surface of its undershell or plastron) can hold a bit of food in its forepaws and then manipulate, turn, and break apart the object with these members as it eats.

However, as indicated before, the prehensile characteristics are not essential to learning the Arrow Maze. Therefore, such characteristics will not account for the species differences obtained in the present study. Only the power of locomotion (and not the ability of the extremities to manipulate objects) is required in the Arrow Maze setup.

If this does not explain the differences that exist, what does? Many explanations could probably be offered. But present-day knowledge is insufficient to make possible any one comprehensive explanation. It is, however, interesting to speculate upon an answer to the problem. There may be differences in other features of the physiology of these animals which are pertinent.

There are very obvious metabolic differences in these animal forms. The rate of motility of the various species differs markedly, especially when the higher vertebrates are compared with the turtles. The turtles have a low BMR in comparison with the other animals mentioned. These great differences in basal metabolism have been very clearly pointed out by Crile. [22]

Crile has advanced the suggestive and productive view that the marked differences in behavior of various classes of animals may be associated with great differences in endocrinic, neural, and metabolic functions. For example, he has pointed out that the sluggish type of behavior of animals such as the crocodile, as compared with the quick-moving type of performance shown by the lion, may be accounted for on the basis of fundamental differences in operational metabolism.

While the phyletic order, as is well known, is based upon anatomical considerations, Crile has advanced the view and shown evidence to support it that animals can be arranged upon an energic scale. The question then arises, as Crile points out, what is the relation between the energic scale and intelligence? Crile presents a graph of brain weight of animals as related to metabolic rate ("oxidation in calories per day") and finds an almost straight-line correlation of the two factors. The graph shows that the greater the brain weight of the animals, the higher their metabolic rate; the smaller the brain weight, the lower the rate.

In the resultant scale that Crile presents, we find some of the animals that we have been dealing with in the present study. These animals are, in the order of the appearance on Crile's scale (from top to bottom of the graph), man, pig, (goat*), dog, cat, bird, rabbit, rat, and turtle.

In the Arrow Maze, these same animals just listed ranked in the following order: man, pig, dog, goat, rat, bird, rabbit, cat, and turtle. There is a surprisingly close similarity between the two lists, which induces us to feel that here we may have a partial explanation of relative performance.

The notion of the biological differentiation of energic constitutional types is now appearing in the literature on the subject as shown by the work of Kempf, 1941. [23] He has suggested an intriguing classification scheme of human types on the basis of anabolism and catabolism. His four categories are as follows:

1. The *hardy*, well balanced type: anabolic strong and catabolic strong.

2. The *hypokinetic*, sluggish type: anabolic strong and catabolic weak.

3. The *hyperkinetic*, excitable type: anabolic weak and catabolic strong.

4. The *weak*, hypersensitive type: anabolic weak and catabolic weak.†

---

* See second note to Table X, p. 87.
† The italics are Kempf's.

Kempf, in discussing his four basic types, applies their formulae to the cataloguing of a number of common domestic and wild animals. Characteristics of the metabolic rate, as in the case of Crile's point of view, form the basis of his types of personality.

Are those considerations related to intelligence? If maze learning involves intelligence, and if intelligence is correlated to some extent with relative brain size (Crile employs brain weight as a criterion of brain size), then larger brain size would make possible superior performance in the maze.

If brain size and oxygen consumption are related, is oxygen consumption likewise related to intelligence? There seems to be a good indication that this is probably true. The pig is very high on Crile's graph, as in our own results. We do not offer Crile's work as a complete explanation of the relationships in these animal forms, but it seems to come nearer to a factual discussion of the biological background of intelligence than any other piece of work that has come to our attention.

Crile's rank order, according to his energic criteria, is compared with our own list, determined by relative learning performance in the Arrow Maze, in Table X. This table also includes the rank order of animal forms obtained by each of the other research workers previously discussed in I. In Retrospect.

There, we presented some of the previous comparative investigations of animal learning which have a direct bearing upon the present work. It is interesting to compare directly the results of these studies with those which we have obtained, especially in regard to the rank order of learning ability in the several animal forms. The general agreement in the order of the animals studied by various observers is, as can be seen from the table, remarkably close. The maze method, conditioning response technique, problem box, and multiple-choice apparatus all furnish strikingly similar lists in cases where the same species were employed.

Table X

Rank Order of Animals According to Relative Performance in
Various Learning Experiments, as Compared with Crile's
Correlation of BMR with Brain Weight

Hamilton (1911)[5]	Yerkes (1916)[14]	Shuey('31)[7] Riess('34)[8] Field('34)[9] Koch('35)[10]	Liddell, James, and Anderson (1934)[11]	Fink (1943)	Hypothetical Combination of Data (Tentative)	Crile* (1941)[22]
Man	Apes and Monkeys(?)	Monkey	Pig	Man	Man	Man
Monkey		Cat	Dog	Pig	Ape	Horse
Dog	Pig	Rat	Sheep; Goat	Dog	Monkey	Ape
Cat	Crow	Guinea pig	Rabbit	(Goat)	Pig	Pig
Horse	Rat		James ('34, '37)[12,13]	Chicken and Rat	Dog	Sheep (Goat?) †
			Guinea pig	(Rabbit)	Sheep; Goat	Dog
			Opossum(?)	Cat	Birds (Crow and Chick)	Cat
				Turtle	Rat	Birds
					Rabbit	Rabbit
					Cat	Opossum
					Horse	Guinea pig
					Guinea pig	Rat
					Opossum(?)	Turtle
					Turtle	

* On basis of correlation between BMR and brain weight.

† Crile did not employ the goat, but only the sheep; this is purely a guess, on the basis of Liddell, James, and Anderson's 1934 paper.[11]

The one glaring discrepancy seems to be the high rank-ing of the rat (superior to the cat) in the Arrow Maze, while in Jenkins' Triple-Plate Problem Box, the cat, apparently, proved superior to the rat. This inconsistency may be a function of some difference in the type of behavior required of the animal in the two types of learning apparatus. More probably, it may be due to difference in age, strain, tempera-ment, or motivation of the two groups of rats compared. It is a well-known fact among experimenters, working with the white rat, that there is much variation in behavior and learning performance between different strains and ages of these animals. The writer has found a decided decrease in activity and performance in the Arrow Maze in older rats. The data on these extra experimental animals was, of course, not included in the averages obtained for the present study.

One extreme case may be cited. Rat 8a ♂ of the Cornell experimental colony of 1941 was only 10 months old or 300 days at the time of testing. However, this was 4 months in excess of the average age of the 20 experimental rats, regularly employed in the Arrow Maze. The particular rat just mentioned required 10 days in which to complete the running of the maze routine, because many trials were necessary and too many could not be given in a single day. Too many trials a day would cause a decrease in motivation, and a greater number of errors and time loss. The 20 ex-perimentals needed only 5 days (sometimes less) in which to finish the learning of the maze problem. Rat 8a completed the 4 goals by the end of the 212th trial, with a very low PQ score of 8.6.

The 20 experimental rats, on the other hand, averaged three times the score of 8a ♂ with a PQ of 28. The fact that these 20 rats were at the ideal age for experimentation, which was approximately 200 days, seems to account for the fact that this group proved uniformly good. At this age, the white rat is in full vigor, active, and readily motivated under optimal conditions.

In the next to the last column of Table X, we have pre-sented a composite picture of the general animal rank order of learning performance, as indicated by the studies listed. This list, of course, awaits further verification, and it is intended to be only tentative. The hypothetical ranking is as follows: man is followed by the apes and monkeys, then the pig, dog, sheep and goat, birds (specifically, the crow and the chicken), the rat and rabbit, the cat, horse, guinea pig, opossum, and finally the turtle.

It is interesting to note that the pig consistently ranks very high in all learning lists on which it appears. Also noteworthy is the fact that, although the birds rank phylogenetically below the mammals, their learning ability clearly ranks them with the mammalia. The reptile class, however, remains consistent in that it comes at the end of the list, well below the mammals and birds.

It is a matter of conjecture as to where the opossum really belongs on our composite list. Future research may put this animal just below the cat, or even higher.*

Concerning the low position of the horse on the scale, a comment here might prove interesting. It is common knowledge that Western horsemen who breed, tame, and handle horses as their daily job will admit (despite their admiration and respect for this animal) that, in a critical situation, the horse is at a loss without the direction of its rider. Perhaps this is a matter of temperament of the animal rather than any lack of innate abilities or intelligence. However, observation of the trained Kellogg Ranch horses of California in action in the ring is not half so impressive a feat of animal learning as is the number of tricks of a more complex nature that a trained seal, a black bear, or other performing animal can be taught to do.

---

* At the present stage of our knowledge, assigning the opossum its proper rank is difficult due to the fact that its behavior in the defensive conditioned motor reflex situation (which was the method used by James[13]) was very unlike that of the pig, dog, goat, sheep, and rabbit in the same circumstances. When frightened, the opossum does not defend itself overtly. Instead, it crouches and remains still. Thus an overt CMR could not be established at all. For this reason, the animal ranked low on the learning scale. However, its *natural* mode of defense (the crouch) or its attacking behavior can be readily and quickly conditioned (James, *ibid.*).

In IV. Quantitative Results, we have already presented an hypothesis to account for unusual learning behavior in the animals run in the Arrow Maze. We felt it was preferable to explain such behavior in terms of experimental extinction than in terms of insight or some other concept. We felt unjustified in considering an alternate, less mechanistic explanation in this particular case.

We have previously discussed certain advantages in the use of the Arrow Maze, or similar apparatus, in comparative studies of this sort. It is our conviction that the maze is entirely adequate in testing the learning performance of widely differing forms. It seems to be adequate especially in that it does not, as pointed out previously, penalize certain animal forms for their lack of manipulatory equipment. For instance, it would be difficult to assess the learning capacity of the horse, as compared with the monkey or cat, if a problem box of some type were to be used. It is clear, then, that for the comparative type of learning problem, a method must be used which takes into consideration the natural endowment of the animals to be employed.

It seemed logical that a simple learning problem, in which the only requirement was the normal means of locomotion, would prove most adequate. The Arrow Maze demands no particular skills in manipulation. It mainly requires the equipment of locomotion.

We have demonstrated that there is general agreement in the rank order of learning performance in different animal forms, as determined by the present writer and others, wherever the same animals have been employed. This was generally true no matter what type of learning method was used. Results derived from maze learning, multiple-choice experiments, conditioning, and test trials in a difficult problem box, all indicate that these various approaches to the problem of comparison of animal abilities are perhaps testing more or less the same thing.

It is, at present, a general belief among the psychologists that many different (and little-known or understood) factors are apparent in various learning experiments. However, in each method of attack, certain factors or abilities overlap. We may assume that it is these factors, prevalent in all the testing methods, that tend to produce consistency in the rank-order results.

Whether one should consider the rank-order lists, obtained by various investigators with the use of different methods, as indication of relative intelligence of the animals concerned, will depend on the definition of "intelligence" one is willing to accept. If intelligence is a function of the degree of adaptive behavior that the animal displays in a maze, or in any other challenging situation, then we have been investigating relative degree of intelligence in the various animal forms. When a particular animal adapts to a change of goal location at a faster rate of speed than another animal, and when it quickly grows accustomed to going only to the new goal and avoiding the old one, then we may consider the first animal, by definition, to be the more intelligent of the two.

An indirect criterion, by which one may try to gain insight into the *potential* capacity of intelligence, is the comparative weight or volume, complexity, and degree of development of brain material to be found in the different animal species. The maze behavior is assumed to be merely the outward manifestations of different degrees of neural complexity. But on the basis of such physical development alone, we are confronted by the inconsistency that we have found in the level of the crow in Yerkes' 1916 study,[14] and in that of the chicken in our present investigation. Neural level should, we would expect, place these birds below rather than in the midst of the mammal group.

With the four-part problem of the Arrow Maze, we obtained the following rank order of animals: man, pig, dog, goat, chick and rat (at the same level of performance), rabbit, cat, water turtles, and land tortoises. The hypothetical list (see Table X), which combines the present study with previous work, gives us the following picture of relative ability in various types of learning situations: man, ape and monkey, pig, dog, sheep and goat, birds (crow and chicken, specifically), rodents (as the rat and rabbit), cat, horse, guinea pig, opossum, water turtles, and finally the land tortoises.

Considered broadly, the general list places the primates at the top, followed by the lower mammals and the birds, and closes with the reptile class.

The fact that comparative work on learning—employing the same apparatus and techniques—has been meager, and also the fact that psychological work on the reptile class is almost nonexistent at this writing, have both been powerful factors in prompting the present study.

There is no attempt to write "Finis" at the end of this research; it is only just begun, and much remains to be done in this and allied problems by investigators with sufficient interest and patience. It is hoped that this work will be a means of further stimulating the attack on the comparative problem of learning which has been unduly delayed. The delay, of course, has been a reasonable one, considering the many difficulties involved, but it is hoped that the present suggestions regarding technique may be of service in future work.

VI. SUMMARY

IN THIS WORK THE CENTRAL PROBLEM WAS TO COMPARE THE learning ability of a fairly wide variety of animal forms, and particularly to determine the rate or speed of learning in one animal type in direct relation to that of other types. We were especially interested in comparing the learning performance of the turtle with that of certain higher vertebrates, including man.

For this purpose we considered the maze method to be the most advantageous, because it does not require manipulatory performance of any kind. Clearly, had such been required, those animals in the experimental series contemplated which did not possess prehensile members would be at an obvious disadvantage on that score. The method required only the animal's natural means of locomotion.

A simple maze, called the Arrow Maze, was employed. It consisted of four parallel pathways leading off from a neutral area wherein the animal was placed. At the end of one of the pathways or alleys, food was placed as an incentive in such a way that the animal could not see it until he had come to the end of the alley. The animal in the neutral starting area had to discover which of the paths led to the food, and then had to learn that pathway.

The animals tested in this apparatus included man, the domestic pig, dog, goat, white rat, chicken, rabbit, cat, and a selection of water turtles and land tortoises from both coastal regions of the United States.

The maze was simple enough to enable us to include the reptile class among the subjects. A more complex learning situation might have necessitated the exclusion of this group, concerning which we were most interested. At the same time, the problem presented to the subjects in the Arrow Maze was such that it afforded a challenge for even the higher animals. The learning scores of the various animals which were obtained were diverse enough to differentiate clearly the animal forms at different levels of the biological scale.

Four successive goals were presented for each subject to learn. This tended to neutralize the effects that may result from the customary use of but a single goal. The animal, slow at first, has the chance to demonstrate its optimal performance in the learning of the later goals. If the subject should be somewhat timid at first in the strange apparatus, then a longer testing procedure, such as the one that we employed, would serve to remove this initial handicap to learning.

Three criteria of relative learning ability were used: the Performance Quotient (PQ), Trial Quotient (TQ), and Alley Quotient (AQ). These three measures of performance had a high intercorrelation, namely, .95. Each of these quotients employed the results for man as the standard, arbitrarily setting man's score at 100 so that all the other animals were thus related to man's score. The formulae which we devised for these measures were such as to give scores ranging from 0 to 100. The scores for each of the other animal subjects were thus *percentages* of the score for man.

Due to the reciprocal arrangement of the formulae, a large number of errors indicated a low PQ, TQ, or AQ score, depending upon the nature of the errors in question. The PQ involved the total number of trials required for the animal to learn all four successive goals. The TQ employed this same value, but with the exclusion of all perfect trials among the incorrect ones. The AQ considered the number of errors in the form of alleys entered while the animal was in search of the food at the goal. The average Q-score for each animal was the average of its PQ, TQ, and AQ scores.

In order to compare directly the learning performance of the slow-moving turtles with the higher vertebrates, time limits per trial in the maze were imposed upon each animal form in accordance with its relative rate of speed. For example, the chelonians were permitted 30 minutes in which to complete each trial (this figure being the standard of reference for the determination of the other values), while the more active dog was allowed only 1.3 minutes. The same maze and procedure was used in the case of all the animal forms with the exception of man. The human subjects were blindfolded and tested in a finger maze, bearing the same four-path pattern as the Arrow Maze. The criterion of successful learning for all subjects, including man, was a series of 10 successive correct trials to each goal without errors.

On the basis of the average Q-score for each species, the animals were ranked in order of ability of performance in the Arrow Maze. This rank order was as follows: man, pig, dog, chicken and rat (the latter two animals were at the same level), cat, two water turtle species (the Louisiana Troost Turtle and the Pacific Pond Turtle), and finally two land tortoise forms (the California Desert Tortoise and the New Jersey Box Tortoise).

The above-mentioned animals included 151 of the subjects tested in the Arrow Maze. However, for the purpose of preliminary investigation, a few single specimens of other animals were employed. Two water turtle species, the Eastern Painted Turtle and the Louisiana Map Turtle, both ranked above the four chelonian species already listed above. A single goat and a rabbit were also tested. The goat ranked just below the dog, and the rabbit placed above the cat.

The behavior of each animal form, as it performed in the maze situation, was described in the text. Although the males were slightly higher than the females in their average scores in the learning problem, the difference between the performances of the two sexes was not significant.

The first and second goals were learned in about the same length of time and number of trials. The third goal normally took a longer time to learn than the primary ones, but the final goal was learned in the shortest time of all.

Learning curves for the three classes of animals studied (reptiles, birds, and mammals) were presented, and observable differences between them were noted. The results obtained with one of the chelonian species were also compared with the performance of these subjects in certain other learning situations, namely, in the two problem boxes.

Pavlov's concept of experimental extinction was suggested as an hypothesis to explain certain behavior seen in many of the animals at a particularly crucial stage of learning the solution of the maze problem. The same hypothesis, we believed, might help to explain why the final goal in the Arrow Maze was generally learned in a shorter time than any of the preceding three goals, despite the chance that existed for interference and confusion with previous goals to occur.

In additional experiments, it was found that the reptiles which we studied possessed retention of a very stable sort. Few errors appeared in maze performance, even after a lapse of more than a month and a half.

An analysis was made of the so-called forward-going tendency which seemed to be present in many of the animals. The possession of a directional preference of certain animals to the right or left in this maze situation was also tested.

It was suggested that the differences between the several animal forms in learning ability may be partially accounted for on a biological basis.

The question of the possible relation between intelligence, or capacity for performance, and relative level of metabolism was considered. This is an important consideration in the comparison of the learning performance of the reptile with that of the mammal, for example.

A series of graphic tracings of typical pathways taken by the animals in the maze is presented in the Appendix.

VII. APPENDIX

We present in this Appendix a series of plates, tracing the actual course (pathways) taken by typical animal subjects in learning the maze. Visual presentation of the actual route of the animals is of value in that it serves to clarify and illustrate the previous discussion.

Each plate is an outline drawing of the exact pathway taken by a representative individual in each species. The path follows the course of the animal during the first and second trials. From these drawings the reader may refer to the discussion in the section on Qualitative Results.

We arbitrarily selected for illustration the course followed by animal #1 in each of the 14 species tested. If an animal subject went to the first goal, in alley #3, without any errors, this trial was mentioned but was normally not drawn. All imperfect trials were depicted in the tracings.

A glance at the drawings of the pathways taken to reach the goal will indicate certain characteristics of the behavior of the animals concerned. First, we note the quick learning which occurred in the human subject (Plate 1). The route of pig #1 through the maze exemplifies the extremely erratic nature of the course of this animal in early trials. It entered many alleys, including the correct one. But it did not at first go far enough into this correct alley #3 to discover the food there.

However, in the second trial, at which time the pig was probably motivated by the food incentive for the first time (as opposed to the unmotivated first trial), the animal made only two wrong entries before it reached the goal.

The dog, D-1, perhaps by chance, happened to reach the location of the food on the very first trial without committing any errors.* The second trial for this subject was also perfect. The goat proved quick in both primary trials, finding the goal after few errors. The rat, in both trials, wasted a good deal of its allotted time in the maze, exploring the rear sections of alleys #1 and #4.

The chicken, like the goat, explored systematically, going from one alley to the next (without entering the same alley again), and thus found the food with a minimum of errors. Although the rabbit's second trial was perfect, the first exploratory trial consisted of much random wandering, mostly spent in the neutral region of the maze, and also in alleys #2 and #3 which were directly in front of the entrance. The cat wandered a great deal in both primary trials before discovering the food.

Although many of the chelonians wasted time meandering about in the first two trials, they did less "rambling" than the apparently erratic pig. Since the latter raced through the maze at such a fast pace, there was a greater chance for it to cover more territory before coming upon the food.

----

* D-6, D-7, and D-9 also went directly to alley #3 on the first trial

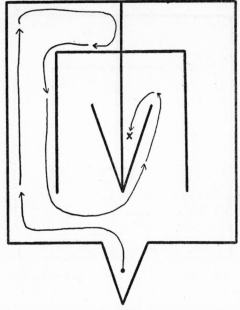

Man. Trial No. 1 (1-3), Subject No. 1
     Trial No. 2 (3, no errors). Not drawn
   The above pattern, which served as the
finger maze for the human subjects, was an
adaptation of the Arrow Maze design.

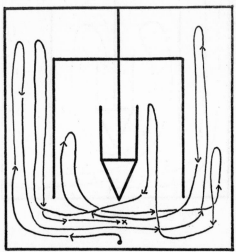

Pig (P-1). Trial No. 1 (1-4-2-4-3-1-4-1-
1-1-1-1-1-3)
     (Continued on the next page)

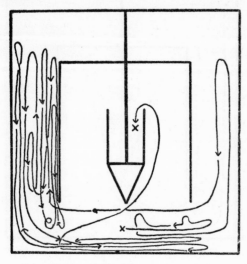

Pig (P-1). Trial No. 1 (Concluded)

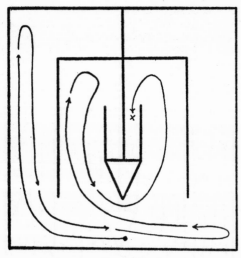

Pig (P-1). Trial No. 2 (1-2-3)

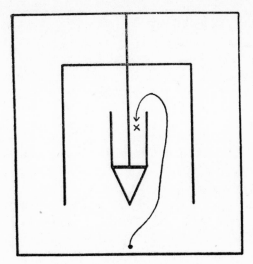

Dog (*D*-1). *Trial No.* 1 (3, *no errors*)
Trial No. 2 (*ditto*)

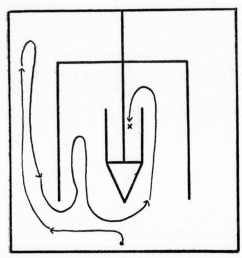

Goat (*G*-1). *Trial No.* 1 (1-2-3)

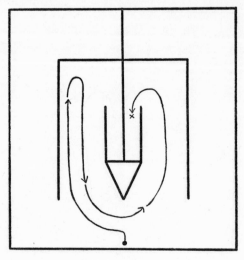

Goat (G-1). Trial No. 2 (2-3)

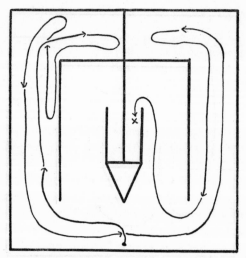

Rat (R-1). Trial No. 1 (1-4-3)

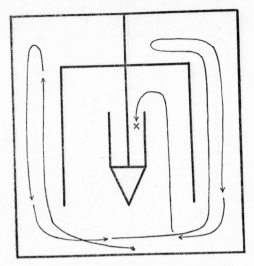

Rat (R-1). *Trial No.* 2 (1-4-3)

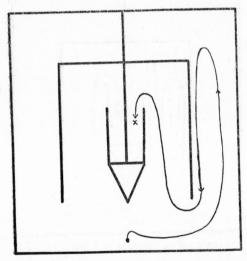

Chicken (C-1). *Trial No.* 1 (4-3)

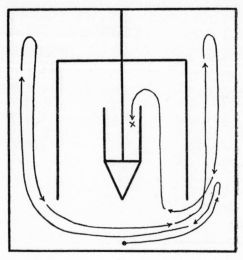

Chicken (C-1). *Trial No.* 2 (4-1-4-3)

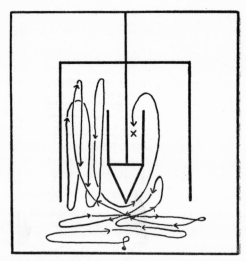

Rabbit (R-1). *Trial No.* 1 (3-2-2-2-3)
Trial No. 2 (3, *no errors*). *Not drawn*

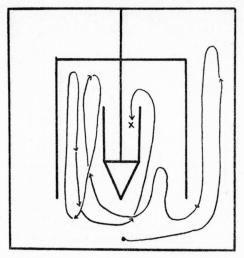

Cat (C-1). Trial No. 1 (4-3-2-2-3)

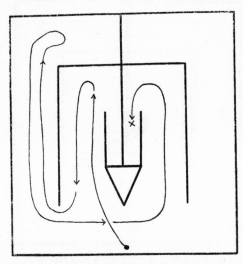

Cat (C-1). Trial No. 2 (2-1-3)

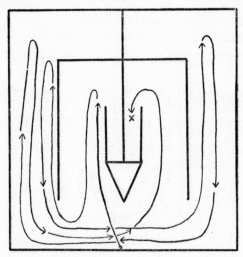

Eastern Painted Turtle (P-1). Trial No. 1
(2-1-4-1-3)

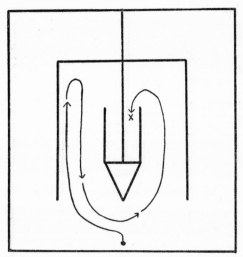

Eastern Painted Turtle (P-1). Trial No. 2
(2-3)

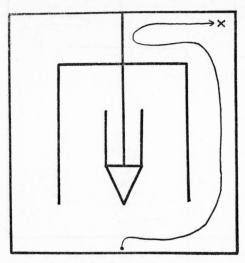

Map Turtle (B-1). Trial No. 1 (4, N.G.)
Trial No. 2 (0, N.G.). Not drawn
Trial No. 3 (2-3). Not drawn
Trial No. 4 (3, no errors; this animal's
first trial under the influence of the
food incentive). Not drawn

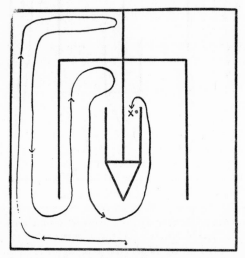

Troost Turtle (B-1). Trial No. 1 (1-2-3)

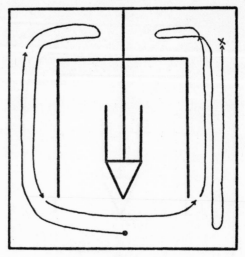

Troost Turtle (B-1). Trial No. 2
(1-4-4, N.G.)

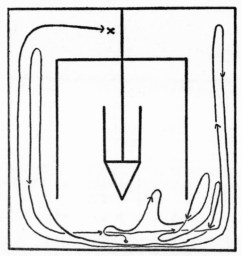

Pacific Pond Turtle (C1-2).* Trial No. 1
(3-4-4-1-4-1, N.G.)
    Trial No. 2 (3, no errors). Not drawn
    Trial No. 3 (4-1-3, the first trial moti-
    vated by food—see next figure)
* *The first specimen, C1-1, remained too*
timid to run in the maze. C1-2 was there-
fore the first experimental subject that we
used.

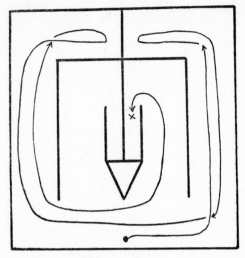

Pacific Pond Turtle (C1-2). Trial No. 3
(4-1-3)

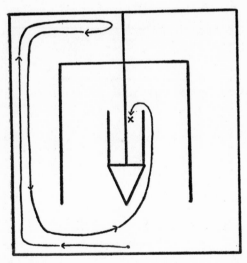

Desert Tortoise (M-1). Trial No. 1 (1-3)
Trial No. 2 (same pattern)

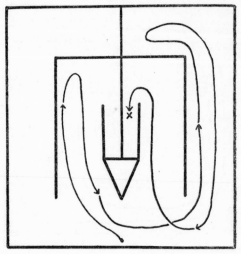

Box Tortoise (B-1). Trial No. 1 (2-4-3)

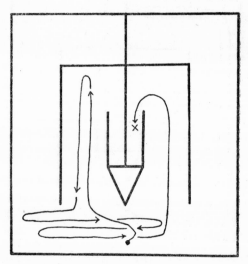

Box Tortoise (B-1). Trial No. 2 (2-3)

VIII. REFERENCES

1. Yerkes, R. M.   1901.   Formation of habits in the turtle. *Pop. Sci. Mon.,* 58:519-525.

2. Casteel, D. B.   1911.   The discriminative ability of the Painted Turtle. *J. An. Behav.,* 1:1-28.

3. Parschin, A. N.   1929.   Bedingte Reflexe bei Schildkröten. *Pflügers Arch.* 222:328-333.

4. Tinkelpaugh, O. L. 1932.   Maze learning of a turtle. *J. Comp. Psychol.,* 13:201-206.

5. Hamilton, G. V.   1911.   A study of trial and error reactions in mammals. *J. An. Behav.,* 1:33-66.

6. Jenkins, T. N.   1927.   A standard problem box of multiple complexity for use in comparative studies. *J. Comp. Psychol.,* 7:129-144.

7. Shuey, A. M.   1931.   *Genet. Psychol. Monog.,* 10:287-378. (Multiple-plate apparatus employed with kittens.)

8. Riess, B. F.   1934. Limits of learning ability in the white rat and the guinea pig. *Genet. Psychol. Monog.*, 15:303-368.

9. Field, H. A.   1934. *Genet. Psychol. Monog.*, 15:369-537. (M u l t i p l e-plate method with monkeys.)

10. Koch, A. M.   1935. *Genet. Psychol. Monog.*, 17:153-234. (Multiple-plate method with Cebus monkeys.)

11. Liddell, H. S., James, W. T., and Anderson, O. D.   1934. The comparative physiology of the conditioned motor reflex, based on experiments with the pig, dog, sheep, goat, and rabbit. *Compar. Psychol. Monog.*, 11:1-89.

12. James, W. T.   1934. A conditioned response of two escape reflex systems of the guinea pig, and the significance of the study for comparative work. *J. of Genet. Psychol.*, 44:449-453.

13. James, W. T.   1937. An experimental study of the defense mechanism of the opossum with emphasis on natural behavior and its relation to mode of life. *J. of Genet. Psychol.*, 51:95-100.

14. Yerkes, R. M.   1916. A new method of studying ideational and allied forms of behavior in man and

other animals. *Proc. Nat. Acad. Sci.*, 2:631-633.

15. Yerkes, R. M.   1916. Ideational behavior in monkeys and apes. *Proc. Nat. Acad. Sci.*, 2:639-642.

16. Maier, N. R. F., and Schneirla, T. C.   1935. *Principles of Animal Psychology* (McGraw-Hill, New York), p. 460.

17. Grant, C.   1936. The Southwestern Desert Tortoise, *Gopherus agassizii. Zoologica*, 21:225-229.

18. Link, H. C.   1936. Personality can be acquired. *Reader's Dig.*, 29:1-4 (December).

19. Ingebritsen, O. C.   1932. Maze learning after lesion in the cervical cord. *J. of Comp. Psychol.*, 14:279-294. (Table III on p. 291.)

20. Husband, R. W.   1931. *J. Genl. Psychol.*, 5:234-243; and 39:258-278.

21. Warden, C. J.   1924. *J. Exp. Psychol.*, 7:243-275.

22. Crile, G.   1941. *Intelligence, Power and Personality*. McGraw-Hill, New York. (See particularly Fig. 37 on p. 210.)

23. Kempf, E. J.   1941. Biological differentiation of energic constitutional types. *Med. Record,* October 15 (22 pp.), p. 10.